# Controlling Skin Exposure

## to Chemicals and Wet-Work
## A practical book

By
**Dr Rajadurai Sithamparanadarajah** OBE JP PhD CChem MRSC MFOH
Health and Safety Executive
UK

Edited by
**Mr Paul G Evans** MPhil CChem FRSC FFOH
Health and Safety Executive
UK

RMS Publishing Limited
Suite 3, Victoria House,
32 Lower High Street,
Stourbridge
West Midlands
DY8 1TA
www.rmspublishing.co.uk

© Crown copyright

Controlling Skin Exposure to Chemicals and Wet-Work
Dr Rajadurai Sithamparanadarajah

First published 2008
RMS Publishing in association with The British Occupational Hygiene Society (BOHS)

ISBN 978-1-906674-00-7

The information contained within this publication was obtained from reliable sources and/or drawn from the experiences of the author. However, whilst every effort has been made to ensure its accuracy, no responsibility for loss, damage, or injury occasioned to any person acting or refraining from action as a result of information contained herein can be accepted by the Crown, the BOHS, RMS or the author.

Any opinions, views, recommendations and/or conclusions expressed are those of the author alone and do not necessarily reflect the policies and guidance of the Health and Safety Executive (HSE), the BOHS, RMS Publishing or any other organisation referred in this book.
This book is published by the British Occupational Hygiene Society (A Registered Charity - No. 801417), 5/6 Melbourne Court, Millennium Way, Pride Park, Derby, DE24 8LZ, UK, to support the "It's In Your Hands©" campaign.

The "It's In Your Hands©" campaign has been jointly mounted by the HSE and the British Safety Industry Federation (BSIF), with the support of the BOHS, the Institute of Occupational Medicine (IOM), the International Institute for Risk and Safety Management (IIRSM), the Safety Groups UK (SGUK), the Scottish Chamber of Safety (SCOS) and the Trade Union Congress (TUC), to promote improved skin care in industrial and commercial organisations. The objective of the campaign is to significantly reduce the incidence of work-related dermatitis by controlling skin exposure to chemicals and wet-work. Controlling skin exposure to chemicals should also help to reduce systemic diseases.

**Warning:** Several commercially available products are described in this book. The purpose of their use is to aid improved communication to illustrate issues described in the text of the book. Therefore, mention of commercially available products and company names does not in anyway constitute endorsement of the products or the companies by the author, RMS Publishing, HSE, BOHS, BSIF, IOM, IIRSM, SCOS, SGUK or TUC.

Cover design by Nicolla Martin, image ref: Sumi Rajan 2007 for hand embroidered design.
Page layout design and production: Richard Westley-Smith, Blueprint Design & Graphics Ltd.
Print work by Two Tone Design Associates, Coventry. 024 7647 4066.

# Contents

# Corrections

Figures 2.6 (page 13) and 6.4 (page 43) Photographs: Courtesy of EnviroDerm Services, Evesham, Worcestershire, England, UK.

Page 118: The word "Corneometer" is a registered trademark of Courage & Khazaka electronic GmbH, Mathias Bruggenstr. 91, D-50829 Cologne, Germany and is the name of their instrument for measuring skin hydration. The term "corneometry" should refer exclusively to quantitative measurements made using the Corneometer® and does not include measurements made using other technology. The instrument illustrated in Figure 13.2 is not a Corneometer®.

Table 13.3 (page 119): The Trans-Epidermal Water Loss scale was developed jointly by Courage and Khazaka electronic and EnviroDerm Services for use with the Dermal Measurement System EDS12 for occupational health surveillance, and the interpretation has been adapted by the author for his own use.

# *Foreword*

Over the last thirty years the number of scientific papers dealing with the control of dermal exposure to chemicals has increased enormously. This research has increased our understanding of how our skin becomes contaminated and what strategies can be used to control these exposures. However, the real practical information to help prevent dermatitis or control the uptake of chemicals through the skin is often not easily accessible to occupational hygienists and so the best control approaches have not always been implemented in the workplace.

The Health and Safety Executive (HSE) have tried to address this issue through their "It's in your hands" campaign, which has been taken forward in partnership with industry, trade unions, safety equipment suppliers, academics and the British Occupational Hygiene Society (BOHS). This campaign was built around a helpful leaflet, and a Toolkit describing how to control exposure to chemicals and to wet-working (you can download a copy of the leaflet from our website, www.BOHS.org in the Publications > Guidance section). The person behind the campaign was Dr Rajadurai Sithamparanadarajah (Bob Rajan), HM Principal Inspector of Health and Safety in HSE.

From the success of the campaign came the idea to expand the breadth and depth of the material and produce a practical book dealing with control of dermal exposure.

The aim was to provide guidance for health and safety professionals, particularly occupational hygienists, to enhance good control practice for skin exposure. BOHS agreed to support the development and to publish the final product. Bob has worked closely with Paul Evans, HM Principal Specialist Inspector (Occupational Hygiene) and a colleague at HSE, who has provided technical editing of the text.

The text provides an introduction to the structure and functions of the skin, regulatory requirements related to dermal exposure at work, exposure and risk assessment and, finally, risk management strategies. While it is comprehensive it is also accessible and the author has remained true to his aim of producing a book that is of practical use to hygienists and others. I am sure that this text will be of real value to those new to the issues involved in managing skin problems at work and those who, like me, have dabbled in this area for some time.

The BOHS is pleased to publish this book, which we believe will make an important contribution to increasing knowledge about control of dermal exposure and encourage more effective dermal exposure control measures to be introduced in workplaces. As a consequence we should see a reduction in risks.

DR John W Cherrie PhD BSc Dip Occ Hyg
BOHS President

# Preface

Traditional wisdom and advances in sciences frequently collide: this is the case with the premise of this important book. Until the late 1960s, traditional wisdom (in spite of excellent observational data to the contrary) suggested that few chemicals entered the body. Hence, there would be little need for the knowledge succinctly and clearly stated in this text.

However, advances in modern chemical analytical technology and the genesis of the underpinnings of dermato-pharmacokinetics documented that traditional wisdom, was in fact, incorrect.

Today, we understand that the opposite is the case: almost all chemicals, perhaps with molecular weights of up to 700 or 800 Dalton, penetrate the skin to a minimal or great extent. Now, the challenge is to demonstrate how much penetrates and what the biological implication is for man and animal. Wester, et al - two decades ago- demonstrated the complexity of this penetration by stating that there were at least 10 separate steps involved. This book delineates how to begin to deal with this complex phenomenon - in protecting not only the worker, but the general consumer as well.

The traditional wisdom, as demonstrated by myriads of Material Safety Data Sheets, suggests that decontaminating the skin should be a simple phenomenon; simply rinse with soap and water. Today, we realize this traditional wisdom not only lacks an experimental basis, but is often wrong. Numerous experiments demonstrate that washing may not only fail to remove compounds from the skin, but may, in reality, increase penetration. The challenge for the next decade rests in defining what the ideal circumstances for skin decontamination are when exposure cannot otherwise be avoided. This will be an evidence based science- now just in its infancy.

The literature of skin contamination leading to dermatitis is beyond this textbook. For instance, Lasse Kanerva's "Handbook of Occupational Dermatology" 1st Edition weighs in at over 1000 pages. The knowledge continues to grow. This documents the need for the knowledge of the current text.

We have failed to prevent occupational dermatitis; the knowledge presented here will aid in this important battle.

This knowledge is not only relevant to the industrial hygienist, but into the domain of dermatology, dermatologic research, public health, occupational medicine, toxicology, dermatotoxicology and analytical chemistry.

This book synthesizes several vast databases and provides a highly and readily adapted practical approach to prevent not only skin disease, but systemic manifestations of percutaneous penetration.

It is my hope that this book's general acceptance will rapidly lead to frequent editions – demonstrating what will surely be an important decade of research and clinical application.

Professor Howard I Maibach MD
Department of Dermatology
University of California
San Francisco
California
USA

# *Acknowledgement*

Before saying thank you to all of those who gave support and help, I would like to state the main reasons for writing this book. I set out to write this book, firstly, to deliver a practical book on dermal exposure risk management (DERM) for chemicals and wet-work; secondly, to support charitable causes. After many hours of hard work and patience, the first aim has been delivered. The second aim is being realised through fund raising to support the work of three charities – British Occupational Hygiene Society, the 'Princess Royal Trust for Young Carers' in the UK and 'Water Aid'

First of all, I would like to say thank you to Mr Paul Evans[1] for editing the book without hesitation and remuneration, but with patience, dedication and enthusiasm. This book has benefited greatly from his critical assessment and suggestions for improvements. I thank Dr Lydia Harrison[1] for the careful proof reading of the text.

I am privileged to have two eminent scientists, Dr John Cherrie[2, 3] and Professor Howard Maibach[4] being closely associated with this book. I would like to covey my sincere thanks to John and Howard for writing the foreword and the preface respectively.

I am grateful to the following colleagues for their expert critical assessment and review of Chapters of the first draft. Dr Dil Sen[1] reviewed Chapters 1, 2, 3 and 13; Dr John Cocker[5], Mr Martin Roff[5] and Dr Sean Semple[2,6] reviewed Chapters 6, 7 and 8; Dr Nick Vaughan[5] reviewed Chapter 11; Professor Peter Elsner[7] and Dr A Krautheim[7] reviewed Chapter 12; Mr Len Morris[1] reviewed Chapter 14.

I wish to thank Ms Shiyamala Mahathevan[8], Mr Norman Stevenson[9] and Mrs Karen-Anne Wilson[1] for providing reader overview and carrying out the easy-to-read assessment.

I would like to acknowledge, with thanks, the support and encouragement I received from Mr Peter Baker[1], Dr Isla Fairhurst[1], Mrs Diane Llewelyn[1] and Dr Robert Turner[1].

I am grateful to the following organisations: HSE[1] for granting permission to publish this book under the "It's In Your Hands©" campaign; BOHS for working in association with RMS Publishing to publish the book and providing complimentary copies to its members; the partners of the "It's In Your Hands© campaign for supporting the publication of this book. This joint effort is essential for raising awareness of skin exposure issues and improving dermal exposure risk management in workplaces.

My aim to help charitable causes is benefiting from the generous support I received from many organisations and individuals. The generous support is warmly appreciated. I am grateful to Dr Lydia Harrison[1] for being a joint trustee, with me, of the account set up to ensure that the monies donated for charitable causes are managed with probity.

I am grateful to Mr Chris Beach[3, 10], Dr John Cherrie[2, 3] and Ms Anthea Page[3] for providing help and guidance to get this book to the printing stage; my wife Sumi for creating the hand embroidered art work for the front and back covers; Nicolla Martin[5] for the final layout of the cover; and RMS Publishing for the careful printing of this book.

I would like to say thanks to two of my great teachers, Mr Frank Gill[11] for spending many hours of his spare time to teach me occupational hygiene, which laid the foundations for what I do in this field; and Dr John Thompson,[11] for all you have taught me and the continued lively discussions.

My special thanks to Sumi, best friend and wife, for her love, unconditional support, understanding and most all for patience whilst I sat in front of computers, in the early-hours of many mornings, evenings, week-ends and on holidays, to produce this book; and Jonathan, my son, for his affection and support.

Finally, I say thank you, the reader, for taking an interest in this book. I invite you to help achieve the objectives of the 'It's In Your Hands©' campaign.

Dr Rajadurai Sithamparanadarajah (Bob Rajan) OBE JP PhD CChem MRSC MFOH

Hightown, Liverpool (the City of Culture 08), Merseyside, UK.

1. Health and Safety Executive (HSE), Bootle, UK.

2. Institute of Occupational Medicine (IOM), Edinburgh, UK.

3. British Occupational Hygiene Society (BOHS), Derby, UK.

4. University of California, San Francisco, USA.

5. Health and Safety Laboratory, Buxton, UK.

6. University of Aberdeen, Aberdeen, UK.

7. Friedrich-Schiller-Universität, Jena, Germany.

8. London, UK.

9. Robertson Construction, Stirling, UK.

10. Transport for London (TFL), London, UK.

11. Formerly at the University of Birmingham, Birmingham, UK.

# Introduction

The consequences of a failure to adequately control dermal exposure to hazardous agents do not always become apparent until after years of exposure. Because of this, many employers are either ignorant of the consequences or ignore the potential for ill health as a result of such exposure until it is too late. The financial burden from work-related ill health resulting from dermal exposure to chemicals and wet-work runs into millions of pounds. The consequences are severe for national economies, employers, employees and their families. Employers have been prosecuted for the failure to implement adequate dermal exposure control. Millions of workers are concerned about dermal exposure to chemicals and the harm that results from the exposure. According to recent statistics, formulated by the US Department of Labor, both the prevalence and incidence rates of skin disease exceeded recorded respiratory illnesses. In 2003, 43,400 recordable skin diseases were reported, compared to 19,000 respiratory illnesses. In Great Britain, over 29,000 people are suffering from work-related skin disease caused by dermal exposure to hazardous agents and each year over 3500 new cases are reported. It is worth noting that these statistics suffer from significant under reporting and there are no statistics on systemic diseases caused by dermal uptake of chemicals. On the other hand, many health and safety professionals are unaware of the ways in which skin comes into contact with chemicals or do not pay heed to dermal exposure issues. There is a lack of understanding that dermal exposure can contribute significantly to inadvertent inhalation and ingestion exposure.

Some consider that using personal protective equipment (PPE) is the way to control dermal exposure; and the purpose of local exhaust ventilation systems is to control inhalation exposure. These views were confirmed when I ran seminars in various parts of the UK. Fortunately, these attitudes are rapidly changing and this should be continually addressed.

Although there have been two decades of real progress in research and standards on dermal exposure risk management (DERM) issues, the knowledge mainly remained with those who have academic and/or research interests. Therefore, this book is written to fill a gap. It provides practical help for health and safety professionals, especially those in frontline health and safety management and preparing for professional health and safety qualifications. Furthermore, it should prove a valuable and a lasting resource for professionals wishing to raise health and safety standards at work.

Readers will find that the style of writing is intended for an easy read. However, I suggest that first time readers take the following approach to make full use of this book. First of all, have a good look at all the figures and their captions starting at Figure 1.1. Then, read the introduction to each of the Chapters. After that, enjoy reading the book and most of all, please use the knowledge gained to implement sensible risk management approaches for controlling skin exposure to chemicals and wet-work. Good health and safety standards at work are accepted as a cornerstone of civilised societies.

# Part 1

# HUMAN SKIN AND THE EFFECTS OF CHEMICALS

# *Chapter 1*

# Human Skin

## INTRODUCTION

This Chapter provides a simplified overview of the structure and functions of human skin. An understanding of its basic structure and primary functions is essential to appreciate the need for effective dermal exposure control measures against chemicals, ***wet-work*** (*see note opposite*) and other hazards such as ***biological agents***. The skin (from the Latin, for "roof") is the largest organ of the human body. In an average adult weighing about 65 kg, it covers an area of just under 2m². This is equivalent to the size of a large beach towel and accounts for about 10 to 15% (about 7kg) of the total body weight. The skin has three major sections: ***inner, middle*** and ***outer***. Each section performs many complex functions. The outer section, a part of which is exposed to the surrounding environment, has four or five discrete layers, depending on its site on the body.

Human skin acts as a two-way protective barrier between the body and the surrounding environment. It is a continuously self-repairing, metabolically active barrier, which keeps the "insides" in and the "outside" out. This means that a healthy skin is vital for its correct functioning.

**Note:** Where practical, medical and technical terms are replaced by simpler terms. They are highlighted in the text by ***bold italics***. The equivalent medical/technical terms or the meanings of the highlighted technical terms are given in Appendix 1 – Glossary of Terms.

## HUMAN SKIN

Human skin is a highly complex organ. Its structure and functions can be explained at different levels of complexity. For example, the skin can be treated as a simple barrier or may be viewed as a barrier with three discrete sections, each containing many sub-layers. The three discrete sections are: inner; middle; and outer.

A schematic cross section of the skin is shown in Figure 1.1. In general, a square centimetre of the skin contains about:

1 cm²

- 3 million cells;
- 10 hairs;
- 15 ***oil glands***;
- 12 heat sensors;
- 2 cold sensors;
- 200 pain sensors;

- 25 pressure sensors;
- 3,000 nerve endings;
- 100 sweat glands;
- 1.5 metres of nerves;
- 1 metre of blood vessels.

**Figure 1.1**

A schematic cross section of human skin. This figure was taken from the hand-embroidered artwork, on silk, by Mrs Sumithra Sithamparanadarajah (Sumi Rajan). The whole of the artwork forms part of the front and back covers of this book.

*Please refer to end of this chapter for a larger scale version of this image.*

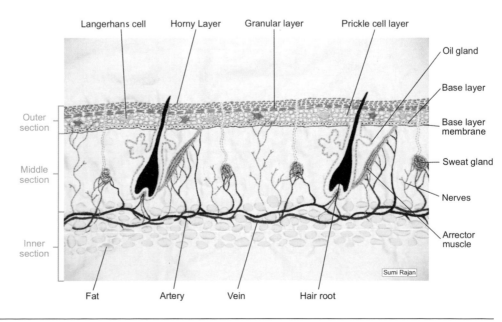

## Inner Section

The inner section acts as a bridge between the underlying body constituents and the middle section (Figure 1.1). It helps to anchor the middle section to muscle or bone and has *fatty tissue*. It is relatively thick in most areas of the body, typically several millimetres. However, there are areas of the body in which the fatty tissue is not present (e.g. eyelids and the sac retaining the testicles). The inner section helps to insulate the body and acts as a shock absorber. The fatty tissue, also, acts as an energy store and can be activated for supplying energy to the body. The blood vessels and nerves in this section branch out to the middle section, where they perform a number of functions, as described below.

## Middle Section

The middle section is about 3-5 mm thick and is made up of connective and elastic tissues. The former provides support and strength and the latter provides flexibility. A number of other constituent structures are embedded in, or penetrate, this section (see Figure 1.1). These include:

- Hair follicles - Hairs reside in these small cavities. Hairs play an important role in temperature regulation. Areas of the body rich in hair follicles have been shown to allow greater penetration (uptake) of chemicals.

- *Oil glands* - These secrete an oily substance that acts as a lubricant for the hair and the skin giving it shine and lustre. This substance contributes to the maintenance of the skin surface pH and provides some protection against bacteria. The pH system provides a measure of acidity and alkalinity and is explained in Table 1.1.

- Sweat glands - These secrete a salt solution at a pH of around 5, which helps to maintain the skin surface pH at an average of around 5.4. The pH of the skin varies according to site and is between 4 and 6.5. The protection provided by the surface pH may be referred to as "acid-protection" or "acid mantle", which is necessary for protection against undesirable *micro-organisms*. Sweating is also important for the regulation of the body temperature and waste disposal.

- Nerve endings - These are part of the nervous system and provide sensory functions (e.g. touch, pain, cold and heat).

- Blood vessels - The middle section has an extensive network of capillary vessels that reaches to within 0.2mm of the skin surface. These are essential for wound repair, the regulation of body temperature and for delivering oxygen and nutrients to the skin tissues. They help to remove or expel toxins and waste products. They can also transport chemicals entering the skin. Many chemicals cause skin reactions such as

**Table 1.1** A comparison of pH scale with Arithmetic scale

| pH Scale (log scale) | Arithmetic scale | Strength | Example substances |
|---|---|---|---|
| 0 – highly acidic ↑ | 10000000 | Extremely acidic | Concentrated hydrochloric acid |
| 1 | 1000000 | Strong acid | Battery acid (sulphuric acid) |
| 2 | 100000 | | |
| 3 | 10000 | | Vinegar |
| 4 | 1000 | | Skin |
| 5 | 100 | Weak acid | Skin |
| 6 | 10 | Very weak acid | |
| 7 | 1 | Neutral | Distilled water |
| 8 | 10 | Very weak base | Soap |
| 9 | 100 | Weak base | |
| 10 | 1000 | | Milk of magnesia |
| 11 | 10000 | | |
| 12 | 100000 | | Wet cement |
| 13 | 1000000 | Strongly alkaline | |
| 14 – highly alkaline ↓ | 10000000 | Extremely alkaline | Concentrated sodium hydroxide |

**Note:** pH is a measure of acidity and alkalinity. PH 1- 6 is acidic, pH 1 being the strongest; pH 7 is neutral like distilled water; pH 8 - 14 is alkaline, 14 being the strongest. As the pH scale is logarithmic, the intervals between pH 1 and pH 14 are not divided equally. On a logarithmic scale, every whole number on the pH scale represents a 10-times change in acidity or alkalinity. For example, wet cement is about 10 billion times more alkaline than the skin.

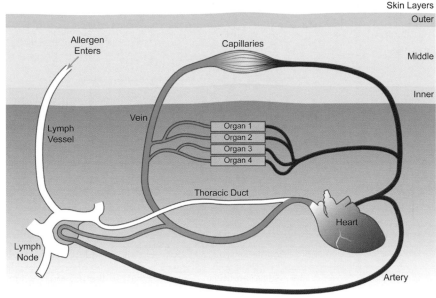

Skin Layers
Outer
Middle
Inner

**Figure 1.2**

This schematic diagram illustrates the inter-connection between the lymphatic system (LS) and blood circulation. The LS is a network of vessels, which runs throughout the body. It has a number of lymph nodes and contains lymph.

Lymph (the fluid) circulates within the lymphatic vessels and bathes the tissues and organs, such as the skin, and carries white blood cells which help to fight infections.

Toxins and other materials, too large to enter blood capillaries (e.g. para-phenylenediamine, a skin sensitising chemical found in hair dyes), are captured by the Langerhans cells and transported in the lymph for presentation to the T-cells (providing protective function) at one of the lymph nodes.

Lymph passes through lymph nodes and returns to the blood circulation via the thoracic duct.

rashes and/or sensitisation and a considerable number, once absorbed, are known to cause damage to other organs in the body. These aspects are reviewed in Chapters 2, 3 and 4.

- *Lymphatic vessels* - These are part of the network of vessels which connect tissue fluids to the blood stream as shown in Figure 1.2. Lymphatic fluid (lymph) helps to regulate *pressure differences* between tissues and the blood stream. It also delivers *immunological responses* to attacks by micro-organisms and other toxins such as chemical sensitisers (e.g. chromium ions in cement). In addition, the lymphatic system helps to remove and transport waste products.

## Outer Section

The outer section is very fine and is made up of multi-layered cell structure. Its thickness varies from around 0.05 mm (equivalent to the thickness of typical tissue paper) to about 0.8 mm on the palms of the hands and soles of the feet. It is attached to the underlying middle section by the base membrane layer as shown in Figure 1.1. The outer section contains no blood vessels. This means *hazardous substances* (e.g. chemicals, chemical preparations and proteins), medical creams as well as other pharmaceutical products have to diffuse through this section and reach the middle section before they can be delivered to other parts of the body via the capillary blood vessels present in the middle section. Similarly, waste products brought to the middle section diffuse outwards through the outer section as well as through the sweat ducts.

The outer section has four to five distinct layers, depending on the body site and these are (see Figure 1.3):

- *Base layer;*
- *Prickle cell layer;*
- *Granular layer;*
- *Lucid layer;* and
- *Horny layer*.

## Base Layer

Base layer contains one row of fully developed living cells known as *base layer cells* and they make up 95% of the base layer. The rest of the cells in the outer section of the skin are derived from these cells. The base layer cells replicate on average once every 300 hours (every two weeks) or so. After replication, one cell remains in the layer (stem cell) and the other (daughter cell) migrates upwards to the adjacent prickle cell layer and from there towards the horny layer. As they migrate upwards, the cells will multiply, take different shapes and gradually go through a dying process.

Three other cell types are found in the base layer. They make up the remaining 5% of base layer. These are:

- *Langerhans Cells* - These cells connect to other cells by means of *tentacles* as shown in Figure 1.1. These are derived from bone marrow and circulate between the middle section and the lymph nodes. The primary function is to capture and present *foreign bodies* to *white blood cells*. This is an *immunological* function.

- *Pigment-forming cells* - These cells synthesise the pigment called *melanin*, which is responsible for the colour of the skin and for absorbing UV radiation. There are two forms: brown/black form and red/yellow form. Melanin pigments tend to be a mixture of these two forms. There are equal numbers of pigment-forming cells in a given body site in darker

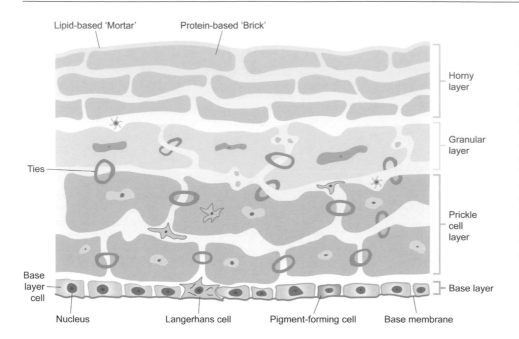

Lipid-based 'Mortar'    Protein-based 'Brick'

Horny layer

Granular layer

Prickle cell layer

Ties

Base layer cell

Base layer

Nucleus        Langerhans cell        Pigment-forming cell        Base membrane

**Figure 1.3**

A schematic diagram showing the cell layers of the outer section of the skin.

Cells in the outer section layers are derived from the base layer cells. These cells take different shapes and go through a dying process as they move upwards to the dead horny layer.

The lucid layer is not shown. It lies between the granular and horny layers. In general, it is found in the load -bearing areas such as soles of the feet and palms of the hands.

and lighter skin types, but darker-skinned people have more active pigment-forming cells. These cells also act as ***free-radical*** scavengers. For example, a person sun-bathing may produce more than usual amounts of free radicals due to the exposure to UV radiation. This excess production can damage the health of the skin.

Merkel cells - These are found in great numbers in the touch sensitive regions of the body (e.g. fingertips, lips and parts of the reproductive organs). They play a sensory perception role.

## Prickle Cell Layer

The prickle cell layer sits above the base layer and may contain two to six rows of cells (see Figure 1.3). They will start to take different shapes when compared to the original base layer cell – a process called differentiation. Cells in this layer synthesise keratin (a hardening agent), an important substance for maintaining the barrier properties. Adjacent cells connect to one another by "*ties*", which help to maintain separation between the cells. The maintenance of adequate spacing is necessary for the correct functioning of the barrier layer.

## Granular Layer

As the cells migrate upwards from the prickle cell layer to this layer, they will become much flatter and acquire a grain-like structure, as shown in Figure 1.3. This layer consists of one to three rows of cells. Certain enzymes in the cells will become active and begin to kill cell components such as nuclei. This is part of the differentiation process leading to the formation of the horny layer (i.e. living cells to dead barrier- forming cells).

## Lucid Layer

Lucid layer is generally found in load-bearing and hairless areas of the body, such as soles of the feet and palms of the hands. This layer contains flat densely compacted dead cells, which are grain-like due to a heavy keratinisation or hardening. The lucid and semi-transparent look is due to the presence of a gel-like substance. Many research scientists consider this layer as the lower region of the horny layer.

## Horny Layer

The migration and disintegration of the base layer cells are responsible for this metabolically inactive dead cell layer. Typically, it takes about fourteen days for a base layer cell to become a horny layer cell. The dead cells in this layer are retained for about another fourteen days before shedding. This is a natural peeling process for maintaining an effective barrier function.

Horny layer may be viewed like a "bricks and mortar" arrangement within the skin and is illustrated in Figure 1.4. It may have up to 15 rows of dead, heavily keratinised cells (the "bricks") embedded in a waxy matrix (the "mortar"). It is about 2 to10 microns thick when dry, but may swell many times this thickness when wet. This extremely thin barrier layer is responsible for regulating water loss from the body, protecting the underlying living cells and serving as a barrier against external hazards such as physical, chemical and biological agents.

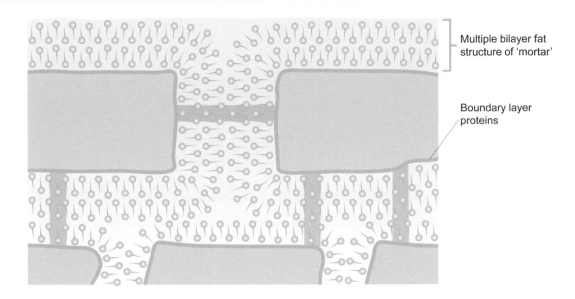

Multiple bilayer fat structure of 'mortar'

Boundary layer proteins

**Figure 1.4**

"Brick and mortar" like arrangement of the horny layer. This barrier arrangement is essential to protect the inner layers of the skin and enable the skin to perform many of its protective functions.

The 'mortar' is made up mainly of multiple bilayer fat, which can be attacked by many organic solvents.

The cells ('bricks') are made mainly of proteins. Boundary layer proteins (those at the edges of the cells) are highly insoluble in chemicals.

The horny layer also helps to maintain the skin's hydration - providing protection against excessive loss or absorption of water.

## CONCLUSION

In summary, human skin is the largest organ of the body. It is a complex organ made up of living and dead cells. It goes through a continuous regeneration process and acts as an effective barrier against mechanical stresses as well as physical, chemical and biological agents. The skin delivers ***immunological***, ***histological*** and ***pathological*** responses to attacks by external agents such as chemicals, wet-work, micro-organisms and physical damage. A healthy and undamaged skin is necessary to perform its optimal barrier function.

## TEST YOUR KNOWLEDGE

(A 'Test your knowledge' section is found in each Chapter. Answers to the questions, in this section, can be found in the main part of the relevant Chapter.)

1. Human skin may be divided into sections. What are they?

2. Name the cell from which the horny layer originates and in which section this cell resides in the skin?

3. List the names of the five layers found in the outer section of the skin.

4. Which is the outermost layer of the skin?

5. What special features help the skin to be a two-way barrier?

6. List the names of three types of cells that may be found in the base layer and describe their functions.

## FURTHER READING

**Dermatotoxicology.** Editors: FN Marzulli and HI Maibach. Taylor & Francis, Washington, USA. ISBN 1 56032 356 6.

**Know your skin type.** British Skin Foundation. http://www.britishskinfoundation.org.uk

**Occupational Dermatoses.** National Institute for Occupational Safety and Health (NIOSH), Washington, USA. http://www.cdc.gov

**Occupational Diseases of the Skin.** Australian Government Publishing Service, Canberra, Australia. WAP 90/032-GS 013-1990.

**Preventing Occupational Dermatitis.** T Brown and L Rushton. Research Report. RR158. Health and Safety Executive (HSE). London, UK.

**Skin Care Forum.** http://www.scf-online.com/english/36_e/skinfunk36_e.htm

**Skin and Occupation.** HB Van der Walle and WP Piebenga. Centre of Skin and Occupation, Arnhem, The Netherlands. Yamanouchi Europe.

**The Integument – Structure and Function, CTS/Physiology, Lecture 29**. Medical Education, University of Virginia, Virginia, USA. www.med-ed.virginia.edu

**Transdermal and Topical Drug Delivery.** AC Williams. Pharmaceutical Press, London, UK. ISBN 0 85369 489 3.

**Skin of color: biology, structure, function and implications for dematologic disease: A review.** SC Taylor. Journal of American Academy of Dermatology; 46 (2002): S41-S64.

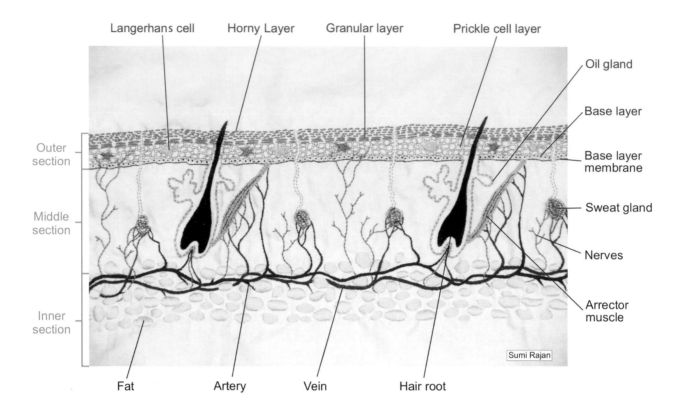

*Chapter 2*

# Protective Functions of Human Skin

## INTRODUCTION

This Chapter provides an introduction to the protective functions of the human skin. As this book is concerned with dermal exposure to chemicals and the associated dermal exposure risk management (DERM), only a brief account is provided on the skin's protective functions against other hazards, such as mechanical forces, biological and physical agents.

Human skin is a highly complex organ and performs cosmetic as well as protective functions. The skin is subjected, on a daily basis, to mechanical forces or stresses and attacks by biological, chemical and physical agents. Workplace exposure to these agents provides significant challenges to the protective functions of the skin. According to the available statistics, a significant number of people at work suffer from the effects of dermal exposure to various chemical agents and *wet-work*.

In order to function as an effective barrier against *hazardous agents*, the skin must be healthy, flexible and intact, as well as strong enough to withstand mechanical stresses.

Skin helps to regulate heat and water loss from the body whilst controlling the ingress of external matter including chemicals, *micro-organisms* and physical agents. The self-repairing capability provides considerable measure of protection against deterioration of the surface of the skin (i.e. the horny layer). The main key to these functions is the unique construction of the skin as described in Chapter 1.

## PROTECTIVE FUNCTIONS

The skin performs a variety of protective functions, which may be placed into six broad categories. These are:

- Protecting the body against chemical hazards;
- Protecting the body from invasion by undesirable micro-organisms;
- Protecting the body against physical hazards including the rays of the sun;
- Protecting the body against mechanical forces;
- Helping in temperature regulation and water loss management;
- Protecting internal organs.

## PROTECTION AGAINST CHEMICALS

Chemicals can damage the surface of the skin. They may also be absorbed into the body and cause damage to the inner layers of the skin and, once carried in the blood, to other parts of the body. The barrier function of the skin depends critically on its construction. The horny layer contains a combination of 40-75% proteins of various types (including enzymes), 10-15% fats and 20-35% of water. The dead cells (referred to as "bricks") are covered with multiple bi-layered fat-based coatings (referred to as "mortar"). The cells are kept together at some distance with the help of this fatty layer and *"ties"* (see Figure 1.3). Proteins, including enzymes, are located primarily within the dead cells when compared to the mortar. The proteins of the cell envelope are highly insoluble and resistant to chemical attack (see Figure 1.4). The enzymes in the cells are pre-programmed (when the cells were initially produced in the base layer) to become active at set times so that the horny layer can act as an effective barrier.

In addition to the proteins and the multilayered fat-based coatings, water plays a key role in maintaining the barrier function and the integrity of the layer. The amount of water in the skin is termed as "hydration". For the horny layer to function as an effective barrier, it should contain at least 10% water. Typical levels in a healthy skin lie between 20 and 35%. In short, skin must be kept in good condition and properly hydrated to maintain the barrier property. It is necessary for preventing skin diseases.

In the main, chemicals cross the skin barrier by *diffusion*. The micro-channels created by the hair follicles and sweat ducts, as shown in Figure 1.1, also offer a potential route by which chemicals enter the skin without having to

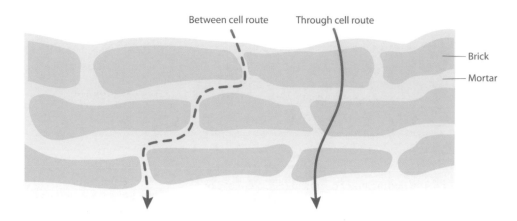

**Figure 2.1**

A cross section of the horny layer cells to illustrate the potential pathways through which chemical absorption takes place.

Chemicals, also, enter the body via the openings in skin surface (e.g. around hair follicles and through the ducts of the sweat glands).

diffuse through the "bricks and mortar" barrier. Nevertheless, the "bricks and mortar" structure remains the major route for chemicals to enter the body. The diffusion through the bricks is known as the ***through-the-cell route*** and the diffusion via the mortar is called the ***between-the-cells route***. These are illustrated in Figure 2.1. Some chemicals may attack the barrier more vigorously than others and damage its integrity. The resulting break in the barrier can act as an easy port of entry.

The effectiveness of the barrier function is influenced by three inter-related factors: chemical agent, the person and the environment in which skin exposure takes place.

## Chemical Agent Factors

In this section, the four most important elements influencing the ***potency*** of any chemical hazard are described.

### A. Concentration of Chemical on the Skin

Chemicals deposited on the surface of the skin create a concentration gradient between the outer surface concentration and the concentration present in the ***middle section***. This concentration gradient facilitates skin absorption or dermal uptake governed by diffusion through the outer section of the skin. Capillary blood vessels reach to within 0.2 mm of the skin surface. Once the chemical has diffused through the outer section of the skin and reached the middle section, the blood flow (around 0.05ml/min/mg of skin) helps to maintain a concentration gradient between the chemical on the skin surface and the blood supply in contact with the skin.

Concentration of the chemical also has an important role in inflicting local damage on the skin. For example, sodium hydroxide is a corrosive substance, but the extent of the corrosive action (chemical burn) and how quickly the burns are caused will depend on the concentration of the sodium hydroxide solution. Other elements include duration of exposure and frequency of contact.

### B. Duration of Exposure

The horny layer may act as a reservoir for a chemical and,

from there, the chemical may enter the blood circulation over a long period. When the chemical is in contact with a large area of the skin, both the area of the skin and the length of time the chemical is in contact with the skin will provide a significant potential for dermal absorption as well as the potential for local damage to the skin. Some areas of the skin (e.g. eyelids, neck and the genital areas) are very thin, soft and well stocked with blood vessels. This means chemicals can easily diffuse through these areas of the skin and find their way to other organs further away from the skin much faster.

### C. Frequency of contact

Frequency of contact is a significant factor for those chemicals (including wet-work) causing chronic effects. Repeated and prolonged contact with chemicals can lead to health effects on the skin and elsewhere in the body. However, a single exposure is enough for fast acting chemicals, usually of a high concentration (e.g. concentrated sodium hydroxide solution and wet cement), and this exposure can cause extensive damage to the skin at the point of contact. Typical damage caused by wet cement is shown in Figure 2.2. This outcome is known as 'pizza knee' in the construction trade because of its pizza-like appearance.

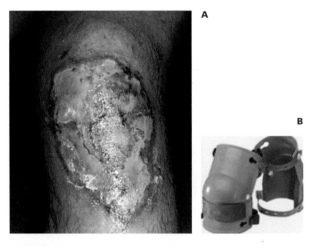

**Figure 2.2:** Cement burns to a construction worker's knee. Because of its appearance, this effect is known as "pizza-knee" in the trade. This serious injury could have been avoided either by preventing the need to kneel down in wet cement (see Chapter 10) or by providing a pair of suitable knee pads (B).

## D. Physicochemical Properties of Chemical Agent

Physical properties of chemicals (e.g. boiling point, vapour pressure, viscosity, size of the molecule, and solubility in water and fat) can affect the barrier and protective functions of the skin. A chemical with a high boiling point which evaporates slowly (e.g. phenol or coal tar), is likely to remain on the skin for a long time to exert an influence on the extent of surface damage, as well as the amount being absorbed. On the other hand, a larger amount of a low boiling point chemical (e.g. alcohol), on the skin, may evaporate quickly leaving only a small amount to cause local damage or diffusion through the skin.

## Personal Factors

These can be grouped into three categories: physiological, skin health and personal hygiene.

### A. Physiological

Examples of physiological aspects that can influence the entry of chemicals are described below.

**Skin age and condition** - Ageing of the skin is a natural process, but it can be accelerated by the way in which the skin is cared for, or the way in which it is allowed to come into contact with chemical, physical and biological agents. The natural ageing process does not cause any appreciable damage to the skin because the barrier

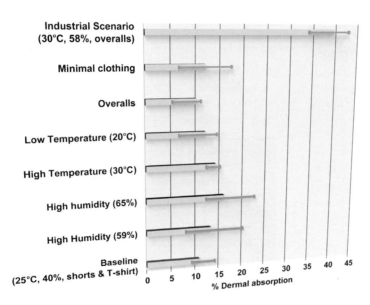

**Figure 2.3**

Skin absorption of 2-butoxyethanol *vapour in air*. This chemical is used widely in paints, printing inks and other types of surface coatings.

Studies indicate that, on average, skin absorption of the vapour accounts for up to 14% of the total daily vapour dose at the occupational exposure limit concentration in air.

It should be noted that *liquid* 2-butoxyethanol on skin, clothing and coverall could be absorbed via the skin (additional dose).

This example illustrates the need for adequate control of skin exposure to solvents, specially those carrying a 'skin notation' (see Chapter 4) and those carrying hazard phrases such as R21, R24, R27, R39, R48 and R68 (see Chapter 7).

Chemical composition, dehydrating effects and reactivity are also very important factors. Some substances will exhibit defatting properties (e.g. petroleum based solvents dissolve fats) and others may act as corrosive agents (e.g. acids). In general, fat-soluble compounds are more readily absorbed than water-soluble substances. There are many reasons for this and the explanation of the biochemistry is beyond the scope this book.

When a chemical is dissolved in another chemical or water, a vehicle (carrier) effect may be observed. The influence of a carrier medium (the vehicle) is complex and it depends on the physicochemical interactions between a chemical and its carrier as well as between the carrier and the skin surface. In general, low molecular weight carrier chemicals with relatively good solvent properties may significantly enhance the uptake rate of chemicals.

Figure 2.3 shows how quickly certain chemicals can enter the blood stream through undamaged skin due to skin absorption. The 'further reading' section at the end of this Chapter lists reference sources providing a detailed explanation of the mechanisms associated with dermal uptake of chemicals.

function is vital for survival. However, moisture content (hydration) of the human skin decreases with age. The surface of dehydrated skin could be damaged easily and this can compromise the barrier function. People with dry skin and those failing to apply moisturising creams regularly are more susceptible to damage by irritants, such as solvents and detergents. Those with oily skin are more likely to develop work- related acne (see Chapter 3).

Blood flow to the skin tends to decrease with age and this will influence the amount of chemicals taken to other parts of the body. Folds in the skin can act as a reservoir (by occlusion) for chemicals.

Damage to the skin resulting from cuts or abrasions will allow hazardous substances to attack the skin more readily and to penetrate the skin more easily.

**Body site -** The thickness of the skin varies according to body site. Chemicals may diffuse much more rapidly through skin areas which are thinnest such as that covering the eyelids, head, neck and genital areas. It has been found that areas that are rich in hair follicles such as the scalp, the angle of jaw and the forehead allow greater penetration of chemicals.

**Race -** There are only limited data on the influence of racial variations on dermal absorption of chemicals. Heavily pigmented skin appears to resist the harmful effects of irritants more effectively than light skin.

**Sex -** There appear to be no significant differences between male and female skin.

**Metabolic activity -** The skin contains many enzymes and a significant proportion is found in the outer section, in sebaceous glands and in hair follicles. However, the amounts found in the skin are significantly smaller than those found in the body's major waste management unit, the liver. The enzymes present in the skin can react (a metabolic activity) with chemicals entering the skin, thereby reducing the amounts reaching the target organs elsewhere in the body (e.g. kidney). However, the extent of skin-related metabolic activity is relatively modest, in the region of 2% to 5% of the absorbed chemical. The rate of metabolism is limited by the fact that once the entry is gained by the chemical it only stays in the skin for a relatively short time before taken away by the blood circulation.

It is important to note that a considerable number of chemicals have been found to cause diseases elsewhere in the body, due to skin uptake, showing that sufficient quantities reach the target organ to cause an adverse effect. The dermal route becomes more important as exposure by the inhalation route is better controlled.

**B. Skin Health**

The health of the skin has a significant influence on skin permeability to chemicals. Many skin disorders severely compromise the barrier properties of the skin. The list below provides examples of skin disorders that can enhance dermal absorption and surface damage to the skin.

- *Eruptions* - Numerous disorders or diseases cause an eruption of the skin surface.

- Infections - These may be caused by bacteria, fungus, virus or parasites. The effects of infection include blisters, itching and bleeding.

- *Dry and scaly skin* - It is estimated that approximately 1 person in 250 has a mild form of dry and scaly skin. This type of skin potentially has a reduced barrier function, which increases the potential for developing work-related skin disease.

- Fair skin - outdoor workers are particularly susceptible to skin damage (e.g. dryness, sun-burn and peeling) due to exposure to the sun. Individuals with fair skin are more vulnerable to skin damage because they have fewer active pigments cells to provide protection against UV radiation from the sun. Another effect of excessive exposure to the sun's radiation is skin tumours and the number of people suffering from skin cancer is rising rapidly.

People with any of the above conditions will be found in many workplaces and may be exposed to chemicals. Dermal exposure to chemicals may exacerbate the underlying disease; may result in further damage to the skin; or may enhance the extent of dermal absorption, especially via the damaged areas of the skin.

**C. Personal Hygiene**

Contaminated skin and dirty clothing, including personal protective equipment (PPE), can contribute to skin surface damage and uptake of chemicals via the skin. They can do so by acting as a reservoir for chemicals, increasing the duration of exposure and frequency of contact. Furthermore, they can contribute to exposure via other routes (inhalation and ingestion) as illustrated in Figures 2.4 and 2.5. Excess oil and acidity (e.g. resulting from oil secretion and sweat) left on the unwashed skin may assist disease development and can help to compromise the barrier properties of the skin.

**Figure 2.4**

Clothing contaminated with solvents. This person is decanting toluene into a mixing bucket to make a rubber paste.

The work practices and the process management contributed to solvent splashes landing on clothing and surfaces (e.g. skin, containers and floor).

Toluene contaminated clothing can contribute to significant dermal uptake and inadvertent inhalation exposure - because of vapour cloud generation into the breathing zone.

**Figure 2.5**

Coverall contaminated with dust. This picture was taken with the help of the Tyndall lamp (see Chapter 8) to show fine particles not visible to normal view.

The fine dust released from the coverall provides a cloud of contaminant in the breathing zone.

Dust on hands can contribute to inadvertent ingestion and inhalation. The latter can happen when the person places his hands in the nostril area or when the dust is shaken off the hands.

### D. Langerhans Cells

*Langerhans cells* and the lymphatic fluid play a key role in the removal of chemicals that have diffused past the outer section. This removal process is a biological or defensive response and further explanation is given in Chapter 3 under a description of allergic contact dermatitis. Blood flow plays a significant role in the clearance of small molecules (e.g. organic solvents), whilst the lymphatic flow is significant for the removal of large molecules such as proteins.

### Environment Factors

The important environmental factors affecting the skin barrier function are humidity, temperature and wind speed. These elements can cause variation to the extent of hydration of the skin surface. Lower humidity can adversely affect the skin by causing it to dry out and crack. Drying of the skin will compromise the barrier properties and the balance of healthy micro-organisms living on the skin. An imbalance in healthy micro-organisms can lead to infection and disease. Dehydrated skin will affect the extent of skin enzymatic activities which are necessary for the effective functioning of the skin. These include generating the natural moisturising condition and seeking and metabolising chemicals entering the skin.

During warm weather, people may not wear PPE or cover all parts of the body with normal clothing as shown in Figure 2.6. This may allow significantly higher skin exposure to chemicals and the sun. Elevation of skin surface temperature (e.g. being in the sun) can cause changes to the horny layer and its barrier properties. Similarly, exposure to cold conditions can affect the elasticity of the skin leading to cracking. People with poor skin health (e.g. eczema) may observe exacerbations of the condition in air-conditioned offices where relative humidity is low and in the region of 25-30%.

**Figure 2.6** Construction workers with no top or partly covered upper parts of the body. In this work situation, hands and other parts of the body can be exposed to wet cement and other hazardous agents. In addition, there is a significant potential for exposure to UV radiation from the sun. It is worth noting that these workers are wearing street clothing. Contamination on street clothing may be transported to public transport systems and private homes, leading to third party exposures.

Damage to the skin barrier can also be caused by mechanical factors such as abrasion, penetration and puncture.

### PROTECTION AGAINST MICRO-ORGANISMS

Human skin is a home for many types of so-called *"healthy bacteria"* and *yeasts*. They protect the skin from foreign micro-organisms to which the skin is exposed on a daily basis. Healthy and intact skin (e.g. clean, sufficient amount of healthy bacteria, right pH, right amount of moisture and oil) is an effective barrier against these foreign micro-organisms. However, any skin damage, skin disease or an 'unhealthy' skin due to poor personal hygiene can create an ideal environment for foreign bacteria, fungus, parasites and other micro-organisms to multiply. They can take hold and attack the skin or internal organs, if entry is gained. Skin, compromised in this way, is an easy target for damage by chemicals, wet-work, process-generated substances such as welding fume, wood and foundry dusts and other agents.

### PROTECTION AGAINST THE SUN AND UV RADIATION

Pigment-generating cells synthesise *melanin*. They make contact with adjacent outer section cells when needed and can rapidly pass the pigment to the adjacent cells for darkening the skin. Exposure to sunlight (including artificial sunlight) increases the relative proportion of melanin pigments and the cells producing them. Melanin pigments act as a defensive mechanism against UV radiation and free radicals formed by exposure to the sun. Although dermal exposure to the sun's UV radiation is essential for synthesising vitamin-D, excessive exposure is extremely hazardous to the skin and general health. The effects of over-exposure include sunburn, blistering, accelerated aging of the skin and skin cancer.

UV sources found in workplaces (e.g. printing with UV-curing inks, hospital equipment and electric arc welding) present a potential for exposure to UV radiation. This exposure can adversely affect the skin and eyes.

### TEMPERATURE REGULATION

Humans are warm-blooded animals: hence, correct temperature regulation is vital to ensure that the deep body temperature is tightly controlled between 37°C (98.6°F) and 37.7°C (100°F). Any departure will result in either hypothermia or heat stress. A large evaporative surface and an extensive blood vessel network of the skin are essential for the effective regulation of body temperature.

Where excess thermal load is created by normal

metabolism, exercise and exposure to heat, or in some other way, this excess heat should be dissipated quickly. Sweating plays a significant role in this matter. When sweat on the surface of the skin evaporates, it creates a cooling effect. As explained in Chapter 1, sweat glands are found over most of the body surface, typically at a density of 100-200 per square centimetre of the skin. These glands are stimulated in response to heat, cold and emotional stresses, during which the body can go hot or cold.

If the skin temperature drops, a variety of responses are initiated to maintain a heat balance and to maintain the core (inner) body temperature. These responses include:

- Constriction of blood vessels to decrease the flow of heat away from the body;

- Cessation of sweating;

- Shivering to increase heat production;

- Creating an air space by the erection of hairs. This action will increase the insulation capabilities and reduce convective heat loss to the surrounding environment; and

- Production of various internal chemicals to increase heat production.

## CONCLUSION

Human skin is a complex organ and performs a variety of protective functions. This Chapter provides an introduction to the protective functions of the skin. It helps reinforce the message that a healthy and undamaged skin is necessary for maintaining an optimal barrier against chemical, biological and physical agents. A compromised skin barrier (e.g. dehydrated or damaged) will increase damage caused by chemicals and wet-work and help to accelerate dermal absorption of chemicals. Chemicals entering the skin may be subjected to a certain amount of metabolic activity within the skin and this activity will help to reduce the amount of chemicals reaching the target organ. However, it should be remembered that many chemicals entering the skin reach other parts of the body in sufficient quantities to cause damage elsewhere in the body.

## TEST YOUR KNOWLEDGE

1. List examples of the physicochemical properties of a chemical that influence the dermal uptake (diffusion) of chemicals.

2. What are the major protective functions of the skin?

3. Protective function of the skin is influenced by three inter-related factors. What are they?

## FURTHER READING

**Concepts in skin care maintenance.** Z Draelos. Cutis; 76 (2005): 19-25.

**Dermal Absorption, Environmental Health Criteria No. 235/2007.** World Health Organisation, New York, USA. ISBN 978 92 4 1572354.

**Dermal exposure to chemicals in the workplace: just how important is skin absorption?** S Semple. Occupational and Environmental Medicine; 61 (2004): 376-382.

**Dermatotoxicolgy.** Editors: FN Marzulli and HI Maibach. Taylor & Francis, Washington, USA. ISBN 1 56032 356 6.

**Epidermal barrier function: intercellular epidermal lipid structures, origin, composition and metabolism.** PM Elias. Journal of Controlled Release; 15 (1991): 199-208.

**Examining issues in percutaneous transport using mathematical models.** MB Reddy. PhD Thesis (2000). Colorado School of Mines, Golden, Colorado, USA.

**Factors affecting the extent of dermal absorption of solvent vapours: A human volunteers study.** K Jones, J Cocker, LJ Dodd, I Fraser. Annals of Occupational Hygiene; 47 (2003): 145-150.

**Handbook of Occupational Dermatology.** Editors: L Kanerva, P Elsner, JE Wahlberg, HI Maibach. Springer, Germany. ISBN 3 540 64046 0.

**Intra-individual variation of irritant threshold and relationship to trans-epidermal water loss measurement of skin irritation.** HR Smith, M Rawson, DA Basketter and JP McFadden. Contact Dermatitis; 51 (2004): 26-29.

**In vitro dermal absorption of liquids.** Contract Research Report. RR350 (2001). HSE Books, Sudbury, UK.

**KidsHealth.** www.kidshealth.org

**Occupational and Industrial Dermatology.** Editors: HI Maibach and GA Gellin. Year Book Medical Publishers Inc. Chicago, USA. ISBN 0 81515 727 4.

**Occupational Skin Disease.** Editor: RM Adams. WB Saunders Company, London, UK. ISBN 0 7216 7037 7.

**Occupational skin infections.** MJ Harries, JT Lear. Occupational Medicine; 54 (2004): 441-449.

**Sex of the individual as a factor in allergic contact dermatitis.** BS Modjtahedi, SP Modjtahedi and HI Maibach. Contact Dermatitis; 50 (2004): 53-59.

**Skin Barrier function as a self-organising system.** M Denda. Forma; 15 (2000): 227-223.

**Textbook of Contact Dermatitis.** Editors: RJG Rycroft, T Menné, PJ Frosch, JP Lepoittevin. Springer-Verlag, Berlin, Germany. ISBN 3 540 66842 X.

**The effect of prolonged water exposure on human skin.** I willis and MC Major. Journal of Investigative Dermatology; 60 (1973): 166-171.

**The influence of skin moisture on the dermal absorption of propoxur in human volunteers: a consideration for biological monitoring practices.** WJA Meuling, AC Fransen, DH Brouwer, JJ Van Hemmen. The Science of the Total Environment; 1 (1997): 165-172.

**The UV index.** British Skin Foundation. www.britishskinfoundation.org.uk

**Transdermal and Topical Drug Delivery.** AC Williams. Pharmaceutical Press, London, UK. ISBN 0 85369 489 3.

*Chapter 3*

# Diseases Caused by Dermal Exposure to Chemicals

## INTRODUCTION

This Chapter provides an overview of occupational diseases resulting from workplace dermal exposure to chemicals and **wet-work**. It is written with two main aims: the first is to help the reader to develop a basic understanding of the types of disease associated with dermal exposure; the second is to provide an introduction for developing an appreciation of the extent of these diseases and the costs associated with them. A combination of the knowledge and the control actions taken should deliver significant reductions in occupational ill health arising from dermal exposure to chemicals and wet-work.

Dermal exposure to chemicals and wet-work can cause a range of problems, including dryness, irritation, redness and even burns to the skin. In some cases, dryness, irritation and redness can progress to blistering and bleeding. These are some of the visible effects or symptoms seen at various stages of the damage to the skin. Repeated skin contact with irritant chemical agents and wet-work tends to start with minor damage, unnoticed by the person. It then progresses to disease because the self-repairing capability of the skin is no longer able to repair the ongoing damage to the barrier properties of the skin. This progressive damage and gradual disease development is pictorially illustrated in Figure 3.1.

Chemicals penetrating the skin can cause sensitisation of the skin and/or damage to other parts of the body to which they are transported. A relationship between the rate of dermal uptake (also known as dermal absorption) and the resulting health effects elsewhere in the body is not well established for a large number of chemicals. However, policy makers and researchers have now accepted the need for a better understanding of the underlying biological issues such as dose-effect relationship of dermal uptake of chemicals. This developing knowledge is likely to influence future regulatory developments in the area of control of dermal exposure to chemicals.

**Figure 3.1**

An illustration to show progressive development of irritant contact dermatitis (ICD) caused by repeated attacks by a skin irritant.

A - depicts normally healthy skin; rising parts of the curve depicts skin damage caused by the skin irritant; the tumbling parts of the curve depicts skin making a partial recovery from the previous attack. From B to E, the attacks and the partial recovery take place without any visible signs. The curve above the horizontal line depict ICD that is visible.

*This illustration is based on Malten and den Arend (1985); and JSC English (2004).*

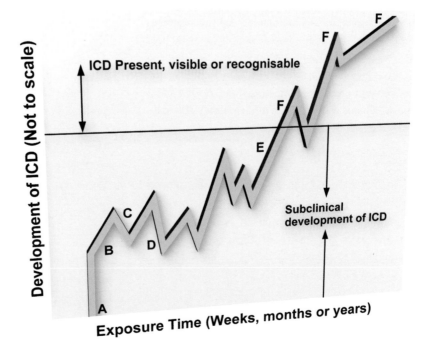

## TERMS AND DEFINITIONS

### Acute and Chronic Effects and Diseases

The term acute describes an effect or a disease of rapid onset and often of brief duration, typically minutes or days. Examples include: nettle rash, sensitivity reaction to proteins and chemical burns caused by material such as cement and cleaning products containing acid or alkaline substances.

The term chronic describes an effect or a disease taking a long time (gradual onset), typically, months to years, to develop. For example, irritant contact dermatitis (ICD) on the hands of hairdressers is caused by daily and frequent exposure to wet-work, shampoo and other chemicals but may not manifest itself for some time.

The terms acute and chronic do not relate to the severity of an effect or a disease. The severity of a disease is dependant mainly on the characteristics of the chemical, the person and the environmental factors as described in Chapter 2.

### Irritants

A skin irritant is any non-infective agent - physical or chemical - capable of causing cell damage by contact with the skin for sufficient time and in sufficient concentration. Irritants may be put into two broad categories: strong and weak. A strong irritant may be turned into a weak irritant by dilution.

### Acute and Chronic Irritants

A single exposure to a strong (acute) irritant can provoke 'immediately' visible damage to the skin. Effects due to frequent and repeated exposure of the skin to a weak (chronic) irritant may not appear for months or even years. The reasons for this long latency are illustrated in Figure 3.1. Common examples of weak irritants include soaps, detergents, petroleum solvents, weak acids/alkalis and water associated with wet-work. Chemical irritancy may be encouraged by cuts, abrasions or frictional damage. Mechanical friction can also act as an irritant by itself.

### Sensitisers

A sensitiser or an *allergen* is a substance capable of causing allergic reactions in a hypersensitive person. Over 3000 chemicals are recognised as potential skin contact allergens and many of these are routinely encountered in the workplace.

### Allergy

Allergy is a disorder in which the body becomes hypersensitive to a particular substance (*Allergen*). Any further or repeat exposure, however minor, to the sensitising substance will provoke an allergic reaction.

### Work-Related Skin Disease

Work-related skin disease can be defined as a disease in which workplace exposure to a physical, chemical, or biological agent is a major and necessary contributing factor in the development of the disease.

Alternatively, it may be defined as a clinically recognisable impairment of the skin's normal state due entirely or substantially to conditions in the workplace. This definition is placing an emphasis on disease recognition by a medically qualified person, which is not always necessary.

Put simply, work-related skin disease is a skin disease caused by, or made worse by, work.

Work-related skin disease is usually seen on the hands and face. Other areas of the skin commonly affected include eyelids, ears, neck, wrists and forearms.

### Dermatitis and Eczema

The terms dermatitis and eczema, (from the Greek "to boil-over"), are often used interchangeably by professionals and in workplace settings, although a medical dictionary provides the following definitions.

- Dermatitis - An inflammatory condition of the skin caused by outside agents. Often resulting in irritation, redness, cracking and blistering.

- Eczema - A common itchy skin disease characterised by reddening and blister formation, which may lead to weeping and crusting. Outside agents do not play a primary role. The effect is due to one's *genetic make-up*.

It is practically impossible for untrained eyes to differentiate between dermatitis and eczema. Therefore, if a person says they have eczema caused by work, it means dermatitis.

## TYPES OF SKIN DISEASE

The following skin diseases are often associated with workplace dermal exposure to chemicals.

- Contact dermatitis,
- Contact urticaria,
- Oil acne,
- Chloracne,
- Coal-tar acne,
- *Pigmentary disorders* and
- Skin Cancer

It should be borne in mind that many of these diseases could also develop in non-work situations or environments. This can be due to people exposing their skin to such things as jewellery, glues, solvents, coins, plants, micro-organisms, physical agents and the rays of the sun during do-it-yourself work and leisure activities. Furthermore, pigmentary disorders can be due to factors such as genetic make-up or an adverse reaction to medicines, skin lightening creams (e.g. hydroquinone), food and food additives.

## Contact Dermatitis

As the term implies, contact dermatitis is a disease resulting from skin coming into contact with an outside agent. These agents can be chemical, biological or physical in nature. There are two types of contact dermatitis associated with exposure to chemicals. These are irritant contact dermatitis (ICD) and allergic contact dermatitis (ACD). There is no absolute visual distinction between ICD and ACD because making a distinction between ICD and ACD rashes is not always easy. It has been estimated that about 80% of work-related contact dermatitis is ICD. ACD accounts for the rest. A significant number of work-related contact dermatitis is caused by the combined effects of both irritation and allergy. Wet-work is a significant contributor to ICD.

The signs of contact dermatitis include redness, swelling, blistering, flaking and cracking. It can also lead to secondary effects such as itching, bleeding and pus formation. These symptoms do not necessarily occur at the same time or in all cases. Examples of the signs and symptoms of contact dermatitis are shown in Figures 3.2 and 3.3.

 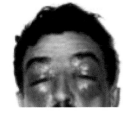

**Figure 3.2** (left) Irritant contact dermatitis (ICD) on hand caused by wet-work. The skin shows redness and has wounds around the nail area.

**Figure 3.3** Allergic contact dermatitis (ACD) affecting the face and eyes. This ACD was caused by exposure to epoxy resins. Photograph: *Courtesy of the European Epoxy Project Team and IVAM, Amsterdam, The Netherlands.*

Skin in any part of the body can be affected. However, the site of the body most frequently affected by contact dermatitis is the hands. There is an obvious explanation for this. The hands are used as a 'working tool'. Because of this, they frequently come into contact with all types of hazardous agents including chemicals and wet-work. An important way to protect the hands and the skin is to employ adequate "safe working distance" (SWD)

between the hands (skin) and the offending agent. The application of SWD approach is explained in Chapter 10 and a poster illustrating the approach is available free for download at the Health and Safety Executive's (HSE) "Skin at Work" website. It is reproduced in Figure 3.4.

**NO SKIN CONTACT = NO CONTACT DERMATITIS**

**Figure 3.4** This poster shows examples of the application of a safe working distance (SWD) to protect the hands. The SWD is achieved by modifications to processes. Gloves are used as precautionary barrier. *This poster is downloadable from the Health and Safety Executive's 'Skin at Work' website – www.hse.gov.uk/skin*

## Irritant Contact Dermatitis

Irritant contact dermatitis (ICD) is a local inflammation of the skin. It can develop after a short heavy single exposure (acute) or due to repeated and/or prolonged exposure (chronic) to chemicals and wet-work. In some cases, more than one agent will be involved as in the case of hairdressers, who often expose their hands to oils, detergents, shampoos, colouring agents and water, both hot and cold.

The irritant action of a chemical depends on its ability to cause changes to the horny layer of the skin. Some substances can also remove skin oils, waxes and moisture from the surface. This action reduces the protective function of the skin and increases the ability of the irritant substance to enter or infiltrate the skin. The removal of fatty substances from the skin can lead to dryness and cracking of the skin. Repeated and frequent exposure to water causes swelling and shrinking of the horny layer, leading to cracking and ICD.

Until recently, ICD caused by chemicals was thought to be a non-***immunological*** reaction and the effect thought to be due to the surface damage to the horny layer. Emerging evidence suggests that among other mechanisms, the immune system may also have a role in the development of ICD. It appears that when chemicals pass through the horny layer they may activate certain types of proteins (e.g. ***"activator proteins"***) present in the body, which leads to chemical reactions and signs and symptoms of ICD.

Irritant substances coming into contact with living cells and tissues can react with chemicals naturally present in the cells and tissues. These reactions can result in skin damage. The first reaction of the body is to produce a defensive response and to repair the damage. The result of the defensive response, in general, is local inflammation at the point of contact. The affected person may experience pain, local heating, redness and swelling. Small-scale damage may not be visible as illustrated in Figure 3.1. When the damage is severe, signs such as chapping, scaling, wounds and blistering will be obvious. If the exposure to the irritant substance is stopped, the skin will repair itself and the signs will disappear. If the contact is repeated, ICD tends to last longer and the condition will also become more severe. Some individuals may develop a degree of resistance to attack by an irritant and this may present itself as "hardened" skin. The hardened skin may appear coarse and thickened, affecting the physical appearance of the skin. This type of condition is seen when the skin is subjected to significant and regular abrasive action during work. The hardened skin condition is seen often among workers in industries such as construction, agriculture and forestry. A hardened skin does not always mean an escape from the possibility of ICD.

Medical books describe several different types of ICD. For the purposes of control of workplace dermal exposure to chemicals and wet-work, this book will focus on acute and chronic types. Any greater knowledge about the subdivisions of ICD will not have a significant influence on exposure control strategies.

Acute irritant contact dermatitis - This type results from a single overwhelming exposure or a few brief exposures to strong irritants or caustic agents. The resulting symptoms may vary from a mild dryness and redness to severe reactions with oedema, inflammation and vesiculation (blistering). The major feature of this type of dermatitis is that the symptoms are located close to the area of contact and they often disappear within days or weeks.

Chronic irritant contact dermatitis - This type is due to long-term repetitive exposure to weak irritants. The resulting symptoms include dryness, redness, scaling, fissuring and minor amount of blistering. Once developed, even if the exposure is subsequently prevented, the symptoms may continue for many years.

## Allergic Contact Dermatitis

Allergic contact dermatitis (ACD) can be considered an unwanted adverse side effect of a well-functioning immune system. The processes involved in the development of ACD are pictorially summarised in Figure 3.5. This diagrammatic presentation is a simplified overview of highly complex chemical/immune system reactions and responses. ACD is also known as Type IV allergy.

There is a period of delay (days to years) between the first contact and allergic reaction. During this period an individual's skin may be exposed on a daily basis to an allergenic substance without any visible allergic reaction. The allergic reaction begins with a process called sensitisation. It starts with the skin penetration by an allergenic substance (e.g. chromium in cement). The entry provokes a chain of immunological reactions and responses and this provocation/sensitisation process can last from a few days to a few weeks.

Once the entry is gained, the allergenic substance combines with proteins present in the ***Langerhans cells***. The substance-protein combination is carried by the Langerhans cells to lymph nodes and deposited close to the ***T-Cells***. In this area, the substance-protein combination comes into frequent contact with T-cells. This 'teasing' process can lead to a person becoming sensitive to the substance by the production of 'memory cells', which will be deposited into the blood circulation and remain there.

Any future exposure to the allergenic substance will be detected as foreign by the 'memory cells', causing them to react with it to protect the body. The ensuing immunological reactions will release chemicals called ***lymphokines***. The result is itching, pain, redness and swelling and sometimes blisters on the skin. The inflammation is normally confined to the site of contact with the allergen. In some cases, the allergic reaction may spread to skin in other parts of the body.

Once sensitised, the allergic condition is likely to remain with the individual throughout life. If further contacts are prevented, the level of sensitivity may gradually decline, but may not disappear. Some individuals may be exposed to allergenic substances throughout their working life and may not develop an allergic reaction. This is mainly due to their genetic make-up and this fact cannot be used as an excuse for delaying, or not taking, exposure control actions.

## Contact Urticaria

Contact urticaria or immediate contact reaction is also known as nettle rash or hives. It is typified by the weal (swellings) and flare (reddening of the skin) at the site of contact, as shown in Figure 3.6. Skin contact with an irritant results in an itchy rash within minutes to an hour. They disappear within twenty-four hours and usually within a few hours. The affected person may suffer from itching, tingling or burning sensations.

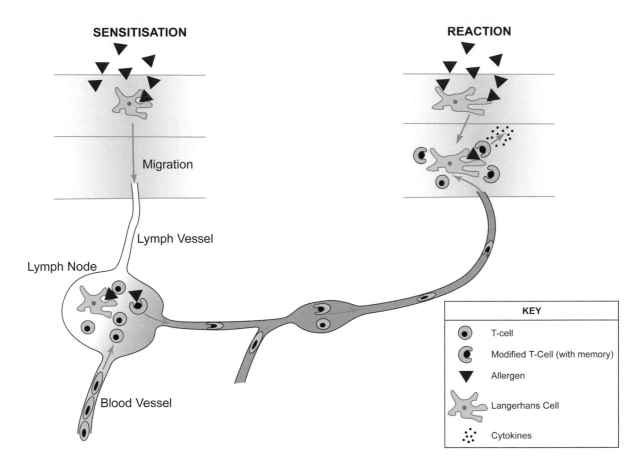

**Figure 3.5** A simplified schematic illustration of the mechanisms involved in the development of allergic contact dermatitis (ACD). The skin area on the left shows allergen entering the skin being captured by a Langerhans cell; from there it is taken to a lymph node, where the allergen is presented to T-cells. Allergen specific T-cells recognise the allergen and produce memory cells. These circulate in the blood to recognise future invasion. The skin area on the right shows allergen meeting the 'memory cell' causing it to release cytokines, which results in typical visible signs of ACD. An example is shown in Fig. 3.3.

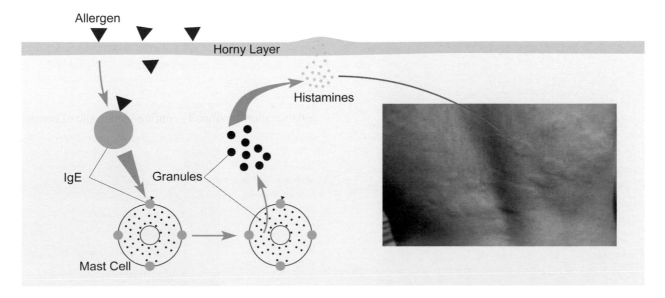

**Figure 3.6** This schematic diagram shows immediate contact urticarial reactions taking place in an already sensitised person. On entry, the substance (e.g. latex proteins) combines with allergen specific protein, known as immunoglobin (IgE). This 'lock and key' combination binds with mast cells. In response, mast cells will release histamine (a protector protein) to provide protection against the invading substance. The copious release of histamine, at the site entry, provokes the typical weal and flare symptoms as shown.

The mechanisms associated with contact urticarial reactions are divided into two main types:

(a) Type I, the reactions involved are summarised in Figure 3.6. These reactions are seen in people who have previously become sensitised to the causative substance and are associated with the release of **activator protein** called **histamine.** In some cases, copious release of histamines may lead to restriction of the airways, causing breathing difficulties. In extreme cases, this may result in death. Type I reactions can occur due to respiratory or dermal exposure, as in the case of latex proteins found in natural rubber products such as single-use latex gloves. Animal and vegetable proteins are well known to cause Type I reactions.

(b) Type II, non-allergic reactions occur without previous sensitisation. Substances producing type II reactions include: food additives such as benzoic acid, sorbic acid, cinnamic acid and cinnamic aldehyde.

## Acne

Acne is an inflammatory disorder of the sebaceous glands. The skin eruptions resulting from acne may be mild, involving exposed areas of the body or severe, covering almost every follicular orifice. Occupational acne includes oil acne, coal-tar acne, and chloracne when the 'trigger' is a chemical found in the workplace. Other types are related to cosmetics, mechanical forces, heat and cold.

### Oil Acne

The eruptions resulting from oil acne are called oil boils. When the exposure is prolonged, skin cancer such as cancer of the scrotum may develop. The incidence of oil acne has declined in recent years because of decreased use of neat cutting oils. The introduction of high performance 'water miscible oils' and improved health and safety standards (e.g. enclosed machining, improved handling methods, controlled delivery of cutting oils, use of splash guards and tight fitting gloves) in the engineering sectors further assisted this decline. Similarly, oil acne amongst oil industry workers is rare because there are fewer opportunities for prolonged contact with crude oil or the heavier oil fractions and this is due to improved production/handling methods. These examples show that adequate control of dermal exposure to chemicals can pay significant dividends to people at work and to society as whole.

### Chloracne

Chloracne results from exposure to certain halogenated aromatic hydrocarbons (e.g. polychlorinated biphenyls (PCBs)). Individual lesions of chloracne consist primarily of blackheads and whiteheads and cysts. Chloracne occurs mainly on exposed areas of the skin but, following regular exposure, lesions may appear in other regions especially the genital, groin and armpit areas of the body. Chloracne usually begins several weeks or months after the exposure and new lesions may appear even though exposure has ceased because traces of the contaminants may still be present in the follicular areas of the skin.

### Coal-tar Acne

Coal-tar acne is associated with coal-tar based products. It may be aggravated by sunlight or UV sources causing an increased pigmentation of the skin, in addition to acne related symptoms (e.g. skin eruptions and blackheads).

### Depigmentation

Chemical depigmentation is associated with a variety of chemicals. It can occur at the site of contact or elsewhere in the body. Chemicals capable of causing depigmentation, such as hydroquinone, produce disturbance to the **pigment-forming cells**. Similarly, chemicals found in food and medicine can also cause the same effect. Certain diseases or their treatment, particularly diseases of autoimmune origin, can cause distinct pale or white patches on the skin. The disorder is known as vitiligo.

## CHEMICAL BURNS

Chemical burns are caused by highly alkaline or acidic compounds. These chemicals can cause severe damage to the skin and the damage frequently results within minutes. Burns present painful bruises, swellings, and/or eruptions, followed by blood flow disruption and the formation of wound-like appearances. Deep tissue destruction and bleeding can occur even after only a short exposure. The initiation of a chemical burn may cause numbness to the affected area, which means the exposure may continue without sensation. For example, chemical burns caused by wet cement are shown in Figure 3.7.

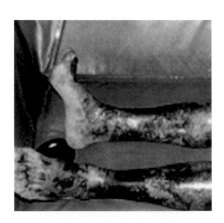

**Figure 3.7**

Serious burns to skin caused by wet cement.

The operator did not feel (until it was too late) that wet cement had lodged between his legs and the boots he was wearing.

When wet cement burns the skin, it numbs the nerves.

It means the corrosive action continues without the person under attack knowing about it. This patient required skin grafts and a long stay in hospital.

## DISEASES DUE TO DERMAL ABSORPTION

Dermal uptake of chemicals can cause diseases elsewhere in the body. However, it should be remembered that systemic exposure to chemicals could take place via inhalation, ingestion and/or dermal absorption. In many cases, it may be difficult to determine the relative importance of each route. However, the relative contribution to the total dose due to dermal exposure increases when the potential toxicity of the chemical is high and the extent of inhalation exposure is reduced. The knowledge of dermal uptake mechanisms and systemic diseases caused by chemicals has increased over the past two decades. This increased knowledge is helping to improve control measures at work.

The principal barrier to dermal uptake is the horny layer of the outer section of the skin. Any factors that damage the structure and function of the horny layer (e.g. health of an individual; personal habits such as excessive washing; use of aggressive cleansers or solvents; environmental conditions), will enhance skin absorption of chemicals. In the main, chemicals move into and through the *outer section* of the skin by *diffusion*. It means that chemicals coming into contact with the skin go thorough the skin because of a concentration gradient. Figure 2.3 shows how easily some chemicals can get through unprotected healthy skin. The major factors influencing the rate and amount of uptake via the skin are described in Chapter 2.

A number of systemic diseases have been attributed to skin absorption of chemicals. Table 3.1 provides examples of systemic diseases that are (or may be)

associated with skin absorption of chemicals. Whether a chemical is proven to cause systemic disease by skin absorption or not, it is always better to control dermal exposure. This precautionary approach is necessary as new chemicals are being added to the list of those that are of concern due to dermal uptake.

## STATISTICS

Occupational ill-health statistics provide useful information about the scale of occupational skin diseases. However, the robustness of the statistical data is affected by factors such as survey protocols, sample sizes, reporting methods, under- reporting and the ways in which the data are analysed and interpreted. Nevertheless, the data available are useful for risk management purposes, which include resource allocation, sickness absence management, control systems implementation, process/product design and training.

It should be noted that there is little or no statistical information on systemic diseases resulting from workplace dermal exposure to chemicals. Most of the information in this area comes from individual case reports.

### Measure of the Extent of Diseases

The commonly used measures are incidence and prevalence. The term incidence refers to the number of new cases (e.g. new patients) suffering ill-health (e.g. contact dermatitis) during a defined period (e.g. first six months of 2006) in a specified population (e.g. printers in the UK). The term prevalence refers to the number of

**Table 3.1** Skin absorption of chemicals and diseases

| Type of disease | Examples of causative agents |
|---|---|
| Damage to the central nervous system | Methyl mercury (an organic compound of mercury), organophosphates, some pesticides and insecticides |
| Cancer of the scrotum | Mineral oils |
| Bladder cancer | Methylene bis (2-chloroaniline) (MbOCA), Benzidine based dyes, beta napthylamines in rubber manufacture |
| Damages to red blood cells | Benzene |
| Heart diseases (damage to blood vessels and heart muscles) | Trinitro toluene (TNT), nitroglycols |
| Damage to reproductive systems | Carbon disulfide, PCBs, some pesticides and fungicides, certain glycol esters, some solvents used in rubber and leather products manufacture |
| Respiratory system sensitisation | Isocyanates, latex protein |
| Poisoning | Phenol, tetra ethyl lead, dimethyl mercury |
| Male mammary glands development (known as oestrogenic effect) | Pharmaceutical grade female hormones |

people with ill health (e.g. existing patients) at a certain point in time or during a certain period.

## Prevalence and Incidence Rates

The average prevalence of skin disease among the general population in Europe is about 10%. The average prevalence for work-related skin diseases is about 0.15%. In number terms, the estimated annual average prevalence of work-related skin disease for Great Britain (GB) (see note below) is 39,000. This is equivalent to about 0.13% for the working population. However, the prevalence data for various occupational groups (e.g. printers, hairdressers and cleaners) based on 11 studies originating from different countries in the world vary between 14% and 65%. The average for these studies is 33%. These data suggest that the prevalence of work-related skin diseases is greater in certain types of occupational groups. In other words, the skin diseases "iceberg" is likely to be much larger than the one suggested by average statistics for the whole working population.

**Note:** *GB consists of England, Scotland and Wales; UK includes Northern Ireland*

It appears that the incidence rate of occupational skin diseases among European workers is nearly 1 case per 1000 workers and accounts for 10 to 30% of all occupational diseases. These data are similar to those found in North America. According to the statistics formulated by the US Department of Labour, both the prevalence and incidence rates of skin diseases exceeded recorded respiratory illnesses. In 2003, 43,400 recordable skin diseases were reported, compared to 19,000 respiratory illnesses.

The annual estimated incidence of work-related skin diseases for GB stands at around 3500. This figure is based on cases reported to the database called EPIDERM. This database, operated by the University of Manchester in the UK, receives reports from GB-based dermatologists who have volunteered to report cases of skin diseases seen by them. In other words, this database is not intended to receive data from every dermatologist in GB.

A survey among inner-city general practitioners showed that skin conditions prompted about 20% of attendances at their surgeries. Another statistical estimate suggests that 25% of work-related ill-health compensation payments are paid to people with skin disease. An estimate from the Netherlands indicates that 7 out of every 1000 employees are absent from work as a result of work-related skin disease. The same source suggests that 25% of the first year's sick leave is due to work-related skin disease.

Work-related contact dermatitis, which includes ICD and ACD, accounts for about 80% of skin-related disease. Contact dermatitis of the hands accounts for the vast majority of these cases. This is not surprising as the hands are used as a working tool. The approximate split between ICD and ACD is 4 to 1, but this ratio can vary from one occupational group to another.

A recent survey by the HSE reveals the following:

- The skin of 50% of GB workers comes into regular contact with chemicals.

- 6% of GB workers are concerned about skin contact with chemicals.

- 12% consider that chemicals could cause skin problems.

An interpretation of the recent data from the voluntary reporting schemes points to the following about occupational skin disease:

- Occupational groups at highest risk are: bakers, barbers, beauticians, butchers, cleaners, cooks, construction workers, dentists, florists, food producers, hairdressers, metal/engineering workers, nurses, printers and rubber chemical products workers.

- The most common agents that are considered to be causing skin disease include cement, cleaning products, soaps, shampoos, epoxy resins, food products, metal working fluids, rubber chemicals, solvents and wet-work.

Skin cancer is one of the most common forms of cancer with over 40,000 new cases diagnosed each year in the UK, some of which are caused by exposure to ionising and non-ionising radiation including UV radiation from the sun. Outside workers are particularly at risk from the rays of the sun.

## CONSEQUENCES OF SKIN DISEASES

The cost of work-related skin disease to the UK economy is estimated to be up to £200 million ($400 million or Euros 350 million) per year. The figure for the USA is estimated to be in the region of $500 (£250) million. Other countries, such the Netherlands, Denmark and Germany, report a significant expenditure due to skin disease. These estimates take account of costs associated with loss of production, sickness absence, rehiring and retraining of staff, compensation payments, medicines and treatment of diseases in hospitals, general practice and occupational health surgeries.

Companies have been prosecuted and punished heavily and, as a result, their public reputation has suffered. Many affected workers live with the resultant pain and discomfort. A considerable number suffer for a prolonged time without reporting the disease and many have been forced to give up their jobs or change profession.

Employers have lost experienced employees, arguably, their most valuable asset.

## CONCLUSION

Workplace dermal exposure to chemicals and wet-work can cause different types of skin disease. The statistics on skin diseases indicate that contact dermatitis is a major problem affecting a significant number of people at work. Hands are the most common site for the disease. A considerable effort is needed to reduce the economic, as well as personal, burden caused by contact dermatitis.

The evidence available indicates that dermal absorption of chemicals can cause many types of systemic diseases. For many chemicals, there are no statistical data to support the association between dermal exposure and systemic disease. However, attempts are being made to build such a body of evidence. In the meantime, the focus should be on dermal exposure control.

## TEST YOUR KNOWLEDGE

1. List some of the common occupational skin diseases caused by occupational exposure to chemicals and wet-work.

2. What is the difference between irritant contact dermatitis and allergic contact dermatitis?

3. What do you understand by the terms acute and chronic?

4. List five diseases caused by dermal uptake of chemicals? Which chemicals are associated with these diseases?

## FURTHER READING

**A guide to occupational skin disease.** Occupational Safety and Health Service, Department of Labour, New Zealand. ISBN 0 477 03580 9.

**A Colour Handbook of Occupational Dermatology.** JSC English. McGraw-Hill Publishing, London, UK. ISBN 0838510 744.

**Condensed Handbook of Occupational Dermatology**. Editors: L Kanerva, P Elsner, JE Whalberg and HI Maibach. Springer-Verlag, Berlin, Germany. ISBN 3 540 44348 7.

**Concise Colour Medical Dictionary.** Editor: EA Martin. Oxford University Press, Oxford, UK. ISBN 0 19 280085 X.

**Current concepts of irritant contact dermatitis.** JSC English. Occupational and Environmental Medicine; 61 (2004): 722-726.

**Dermatotoxicolgy.** Editors: FN Marzulli and HI Maibach. Taylor & Francis, Washington, USA. ISBN 1 56032 356 6.

**Essentials of Occupational Skin Management.** CL Packham. Limited Edition Press, Southport, UK. ISBN 1 85988 045 2.

**HSE Statistics.** Health and Safety Executive. UK. www.hse.gov.uk

**Health and Safety Statistics 2004-2005. Misc700**. Health and Safety Executive, London, UK.

**Health and safety statistics 2006/07. C105.** Health and Safety Executive, London, UK.

**Irritant contact dermatitis. Traumiterative and cumulative impairment by cosmetics, climate, and other daily loads.** KE Malten, JA den Arend. Dermatosen in Beruf und Umwelt; 33 (1985): 125-132.

**Medical Aspects of Occupational Skin Disease, MS24 (Second Edition).** 2004. HSE Books, Sudbury, UK.

**Occupational contact dermatitis has an appreciable impact on quality of life.** CV Hutchings, KW Shum and DJ Gawkrodger. Contact Dermatitis; 45 (2001): 17-20.

**Occupational Dermatoses: overview.** JSC English. Occupational Medicine; 54 (2004): 439-440.

**Occupational Dermatoses.** National Institute of Occupational Safety and Health. http://www.cdc.gov

**Occupational Health Statistics.** Bureau of Labor Statistics, US Department of Labor. USA. http://www.bls.gov

**Occupational skin cancers.** DJ Gawkrodger. Occupational Medicine; 54 (2004): 458-463.

**Occupational skin disease.** WF Peate. American Family Physician; 66 (2002): 1025 -1031.

**Occupational Skin Disease**. RM Adams. WB Saunders Company, London, UK. ISBN 0 7216 7037 7.

**Occupational skin-disease data in Europe.** TL Diepgen. International Archives of Occupational and Environmental Health; 76 (2003): 331-338.

**Occupational Skin Disorders.** DJ Hogan. Igaku-Shoin, New York, USA. ISBN 0 89640 248 7.

**Nonfatal skin diseases and disorders in construction.** The Construction Chart Book 46. The Centre to Protect Workers' Rights. Washington, USA.

**Prevalence of self-reported work-related skin conditions in Taiwanese working population.** YH Shao, WY Yeh, CJ Chen, CW Chen, YL Guo. Journal of Occupational Health; 43 (2001): 238-242.

**Prevalence of occupational hand dermatitis in UK hairdressers.** JB Perkins and A Farrow. International Journal of Occupational Health; 11 (2005): 289-293.

**Prevent Work-Related Dermatitis - It's in Your Hands.** www.rospa.com/safetygroupsuk

**Preventing Occupational Dermatitis.** T Brown and L Rushton. Research Report RR158. Health and Safety Executive. London, UK.

**Prevention of Contact Dermatitis.** Editors: P Elsner, JM Lachapelle, JE Whalberg and HI Maibach. Karger, London, UK. ISBN 3 8055 6311 6.

**Rash Decisions: HSE video.** Health and Safety Executive. London, UK.

**Return-to-work barriers for workers with contact dermatitis.** DL Holness. Contact dermatitis; 49 (2004): 273-275.

**Skin and Occupation.** HB Van der Walle and WP Piebenga. Centre of Skin and Occupation, Arnhem, The Netherlands. Yamanouchi Europe.

**Skin at Work.** Health and Safety Executive, London, UK. http://www.hse.gov.uk/skin

**Surface and Dermal Monitoring for Toxic Exposures.** SA Ness. Van Nostrand Reinhold. New York, USA. ISBN 0 442 01465 1.

**Textbook of Contact Dermatitis.** Editors: RJG Rycroft, T Menn☐, PJ Frosch, JP Lepoittevin. Springer-Verlag, Berlin, Germany. ISBN 3 540 66842 X.

**The impact of occupational injury reduction to the U.S. economy.** E Zaloshnja, TD Miller, G Waehrer. American Journal of Industrial Medicine; 49 (2006): 719-727.

**The importance of occupational skin diseases in the United States.** BD Lushniak. International Archives of Occupational and Environmental Health; 76 (2003): 325-330.

**The perils of contact dermatitis for hairdressers.** J English. Dermatology in Practice; 12 (2004): 12-13.

**The role of the skin in the development of chemical respiratory hypersensitivity.** Toxicological Letters; 86 (1996): 89-92.

**The significance of skin exposure.** MF Boeniger. Annals of Occupational Hygiene; 47 (2003): 591-593.

**Urticaria and angioedema.** British Association of Dermatologists. 1A Fitzroy Square, London, W1T 6EH, UK.

**Workplace Health and Safety Survey Programme, 2005 worker survey first findings.** JT Hodgson, JR Jones, SD Clarke, AJ Blackburn, S Webster, CS Huxtable and S Wilkinson. Health and Safety Executive, London, UK. www.hse.gov.uk/statistics

**Work-Related Skin Disorders in Washington State. Report No. 36-4-1998.** SR Sama, A Bushley, M Cohen, M Cotey, B Park and J Kaufman. Department of Labour and Industries, Washington, USA.

# *Chapter 4*

# Occupations, Chemicals and Diseases

## INTRODUCTION

Chemicals play a significant role in modern day living. Natural, synthetic and/or recycled chemicals are needed to produce almost every item used at work, home and leisure. People at work handle chemicals to synthesise new chemicals; to make new products and clothing; to make and preserve foods; to manufacture equipment and machines; to maintain and protect equipment and machinery; to protect the health of people, plants and animals; for designing and producing publications and many more purposes.

When chemicals are handled, created intentionally or as by-products, workers' skin is often exposed to them. Certain occupations and processes place workers at more risk than others. In this Chapter, examples of chemicals presenting the risk of irritant contact dermatitis (ICD), allergic contact dermatitis (ACD) and the potential for systemic diseases are given. These compilations are intended to provide an easy reference for practical dermal exposure risk management (DERM). They do not provide a comprehensive compendium of ill-health caused by dermal exposure to chemicals.

## OCCUPATIONS AND CONTACT DERMATITIS

Table 4.1 lists examples of occupations in which irritant and sensitising chemicals may be encountered. Occupations in which *wet-work* is a serious concern are also highlighted. Chemicals listed in this Table may be found in various forms at work. These include: pure substances, products, foods, medicines, natural products, by-products and wastes.

## CHEMICALS WITH SKIN NOTATION AND USES

Regulatory agencies use skin notation ('Sk') to warn users of chemicals. Chemicals attracting the notation can be easily absorbed through the unbroken skin, which can lead to various ill-health consequences elsewhere in the body. Table 4.2 lists a number of chemicals which have attracted the 'Sk' notation. Also listed are examples of the main industrial uses. This Table is useful for hazard identification, exposure risk assessment and control.

**Table 4.1** Occupations, irritants and sensitisers

| OCCUPATION | IRRITANTS (POTENTIAL TO CAUSE ICD) | SENSITISERS (POTENTIAL TO CAUSE ACD) |
|---|---|---|
| **Agricultural workers** | Artificial fertilisers; cleaning products; diesel; disinfectants; dusts including soil and food products; gasoline; oils; pesticides; plants; solvents; wet-work. | Animal feeds; barley; cement; fungicides; germicidal products; oats; plants; pesticides; veterinary medications; wood dust; preservatives; wool. |
| **Aircraft workers - manufacture, repair and maintenance of aircrafts and missiles** | Greases; non epoxy adhesives; sealants; paints (silicone, acrylic types); oils; solvents; jet fuels; phenyl napthylamine. | Chromium; colophony; epoxy resins and hardeners; formaldehyde; nickel; preservatives in oils; phenyl napthylamine. |
| **Artists, designers, illustrators, sculptors** | Clay; paint removers; plaster; sand-paper; solvents. | Colophony; dyes; epoxy resins and hardeners; pigments; turpentine; wood dust. |
| **Bank workers** | Paper currency; sharp edges. | Nickel in coins. |
| **Bakers** | Acids; detergents; wet-work. | Ammonium persulphate; benzoyl peroxide; dyes; essential oils; enzymes; flavours; flour; some fruits. |
| **Bartenders** | Detergents; disinfectants; scale- removers; wet-work. | Formaldehyde; some fruits. |
| **Beauticians (Nails)** | Dusts; acetone; disinfectants. | Ethylmethacrylate; methylmethacrylate. |
| **Bookbinders** | Adhesives; paper dust; sharp edges; solvents. | Adhesives; leather; resins; synthetic leather. |
| **Butchers and abattoir workers** | Acids; alkalis; detergents; waste products; wet-work. | Animal proteins; formaldehyde; latex rubber proteins; nickel; sawdust. |
| **Cabinet makers and carpenters** | Detergents; glues; solvents; thinners; wood dust; wood preservatives. | Colophony; dyes; fungicides; glues; turpentine; varnish; wood dust. |
| **Candle makers** | Detergents; solvents. | Cobalt; dyes; nickel; perfumes. |
| **Carpet layers** | Adhesives; dusts. | Adhesives; mites; fungus; animal waste. |
| **Cleaners** | Detergents; other cleaning products; solvents; wet-work. | Formaldehyde; germicidal agents. |
| **Construction workers** | Cement; dusts; solvents; sand; wet-work; building materials. | Cement; chromium; chromium compounds, cobalt; epoxy resins; nickel; resins; thiuram in gloves, wood dust; isocyanate based products. |
| **Cooks and caterers** | Acids; alkalis; bleaching agents; detergents; vegetable juices; wet-work. | Flavours (some types); formaldehyde; garlic; sodium metabisulphite; spices. |
| **Dentists and dental technicians** | Detergents; wet-work. | Dental impression material; disinfectants; eugenol; local anaesthetics (some); mercury; methacrylates; latex rubber proteins. |
| **Doctors, nurses and others** | Disinfectants; detergents; wet-work. | Latex gloves; anaesthetics, antibiotics and antiseptics; phenothiazines; formaldehyde; glutaraldehyde; liquid chloroxylenol. |
| **Dry cleaners** | Detergents; solvents; spotting agents. | Formaldehyde. |
| **Electricians** | Fibre glass; soldering fluxes. | Epoxy resins; rubber; isocyanates; soldering fluxes; dusts. |

| OCCUPATION | IRRITANTS (POTENTIAL TO CAUSE ICD) | SENSITISERS (POTENTIAL TO CAUSE ACD) |
|---|---|---|
| Electroplaters | Acids; alkalis; salts. | Chromium; cobalt; nickel. |
| Embalmers | Wet-work | Formaldehyde. |
| Floor-layers | Solvents. | Cement; epoxy resins; house mites; wood; wood dust. |
| Florists and gardeners | Compost; fertilizers; pesticides; wet-work; soil; preservatives. | Plants; pesticides; insecticides. |
| Foundry workers | Dust; sand. | Chromium; cobalt; nickel; phenol/urea-formaldehyde resins. |
| Graffiti removers | Dust; solvents; wet-work. | Fungal spores. |
| Hairdressers | Bleaching agents; dyes; permanent wave solutions; shampoos; wet-work. | Dyes; nickel; persulphates; perfumes; latex rubber protein; amine based chemicals, including paraphenylene diamine (ppd). |
| Hospital and care home workers | Detergents; disinfectants; wet-work. | Latex rubber proteins; medicines. |
| Jewellers | Ammonia; detergents; solvents. | Colophony; epoxy resin; metals; soldering fluxes. |
| Keep-fit workers | Acids; alkalis; detergents; UV. | Formaldehyde; nickel; synthetic products. |
| Metal workers - engineering | Cutting oils /fluids; solvents; metal shavings/dusts; wet-work. | Additives/preservatives in cutting fluids; chromium; nickel. |
| Metal workers - Mechanics | Cleaners; diesel; gasoline; greases; oils; solvents. | Chromium; epoxy resin; nickel. |
| Motor vehicle repairers | Aggressive hand cleaning products; fuels; oils; paints; solvents. | Chromium; cobalt; epoxy resins; nickel. |
| Painters | Aggressive hand cleaners; solvents; thinners; antibacterial and anti-mould agents. | Turpentine; thinners; chromium; formaldehyde; epoxy products; polyester resins. |
| Photographic industry workers | Solvents; wet-work. | Chromium; colour developers; para-aminophenol; formaldehyde; hydroquinone; sodium metabisulphite. |
| Plastics workers | Solvents; acids; styrene; oxidizing agents. | Epoxy resins and hardeners; phenolic resins; polyurethanes; plasticisers. |
| Printers | Solvents. | Colophony; formaldehyde; metals in resins/inks; resins; hardeners; turpentine. |
| Roofers | Dust; solvents; tar. | Tar. |
| Rubber products workers | Solvents; talc; uncured rubber; zinc stearate. | Colophony; dyes; rubber conditioning chemicals; different amines; epoxy resins. |
| Shoemakers | Solvents. | Adhesives; chromium; leather; rubber; turpentine. |
| Tannery workers | Acids; alkalis; reducing and oxidizing agents; wet-work. | Chromates; dyes; formaldehyde; fungicides; tanning agents. |
| Textile workers | Dust; bleaching agents; fibres; solvent. | Dyes; chromium; formaldehyde; resins; nickel. |
| Veterinarians | Disinfectants; wet-work. | Some anaesthetics, antibiotics and antiseptics; chloroxylenol; formaldehyde; glutaraldehyde; latex rubber proteins; phenothiazines. |

**Table 4.2** Chemicals with skin notation and their main uses

| CHEMICAL | MAJOR INDUSTRIAL USES | INDUSTRIAL SECTOR |
|---|---|---|
| Acrylamide | Chemical intermediate for producing polyacrylamide (for uses such as water treatment, oil recovery and paper treatment), N-methyl acrylamide, dyes and adhesives. | Chemicals manufacturing. |
| Acrylonitrile | Monomer used in the production of polymeric materials such as plastic fibres, plastics and in the synthesis of other monomers such as adiponitrile and acrylamide. Also used in nitrile rubber production. | Chemicals manufacturing; rubber products manufacturing. |
| 2-propene-1-ol (Allyl alcohol) | Used in production of various other chemicals used in resins, coatings, flavourings and pharmaceuticals etc. May be used as a herbicide | Chemicals manufacturing; coatings manufacturing; agriculture. |
| Aniline | Used in manufacture of methylene diphenyl diisocyanate (MDI), dyes, pigments, rubber processing chemicals and herbicides. | Chemicals manufacturing. |
| Benzene | Used as a major chemical intermediate to make polymers, plastics, phenols and pharmaceutical intermediates. | Chemicals manufacturing; petrochemicals industry; waste handling industry; service stations; transportation; motor vehicle repair sector. |
| Bromomethane (methyl bromide) | Production and use is limited by Montreal Protocol. Used as a Soil sterilant, in pest control. Minor uses as laboratory reagent/solvent. | Agriculture; laboratories. |
| Butan-1-ol (Butanol) | As a solvent in chemical and textile processing, organic synthesis and in the manufacture of lacquers. | Chemicals and coatings manufacture; surface coating sectors; construction sector; furniture manufacturing and restoration. |
| Butan-2-one (methyl ethyl ketone) | A commonly used solvent in adhesives, paints, paper coating, printing, wood stains and varnishes and rubber products. | Chemicals manufacturing; coatings; construction; wood working; printing; electroplating. |
| 2-butoxyethanol | Surface coatings and inks; acrylic resins, leather protectors, oil spill dispersants and photographic solvents may contain the chemical. | Coatings and chemicals manufacturing; construction; wood working; printing. |
| 2-butoxyethyl acetate | Surface coatings, inks, lacquers, printing and leather finishing. | Coatings, chemicals and rubber manufacturing; printing, wood working; construction sectors. |
| Carbon disulphide | Manufacture of rayon, cellophane film and carbon tetrachloride. As a solvent in laboratories. May be used as an insecticide for fumigation of grains and as soils disinfectant against pests. | Chemicals manufacturing; laboratories; agriculture; shipping. |
| Carbon tetrachloride | Manufacture of pharmaceuticals and chlorinated rubber. | Chemicals and pharmaceuticals manufacturing. |
| Chlorobenzene | Manufacture of nitrochlorobenzenes, diphenyl oxide and diphenyldichlorosilane. As a solvent in the production of isocyanates. May be used in crop protection. | Chemicals manufacturing; agriculture. |

| CHEMICAL | MAJOR INDUSTRIAL USES | INDUSTRIAL SECTOR |
|---|---|---|
| 2-chloroethanol | Chemical synthesis of ethylene oxide and as an intermediate in the manufacture of plastics, dyes and pharmaceuticals. Used as a solvent in textile printing dyes, in dewaxing, refining rosin and extracting pine products. | Chemicals manufacturing. |
| Chloroform | As a solvent in pharmaceuticals production and in the manufacture of fluro-chloro chemicals, waxes, dyes and pesticides. | Chemicals and pharmaceuticals manufacturing. |
| 1-chloro-4-nitrobenzene (Nitrochlorobenzene) | Chemical intermediate for dyes, insecticides and rubber products. | Chemicals and rubber products manufacturing. |
| Chlorpyrifos (ISO) | Pesticides | Agriculture. |
| Isopropyl benzene (Cumene) | Use in manufacture of phenol and other chemicals. | Chemicals manufacturing. |
| Cyclohexanone | Used in the manufacture of caprolactone (precursor of nylon). Also coating materials, adhesives and some pesticides. Some small-scale laboratory use. | Chemicals manufacturing. |
| 1,2-dibromoethane (Ethylene bromide) | Pesticide but now banned for this use in many countries. Used as an intermediate in chemicals manufacture. | Chemicals manufacturing. |
| 1,2 –dichlorobenzene (Dichlorobenzene) | Chemical intermediate in the manufacture of other dichlorobenzenes. | Chemicals manufacturing. |
| 1,1-dichloroethane (Ethylene dichloride) | Limited use compared to 1, 2- isomer. | Chemicals manufacturing. |
| 1,2-dichloroethane (Dichloroethane) | Intermediate for vinyl chloride monomer. | Chemicals manufacturing. |
| Dichloromethane (methylene chloride) | Widely used as a solvent in chemicals and pharmaceutical industries. As a paint stripping solvent; as a paint brush restorer; may be used as extractant of flavours such coffee. | Chemical processing; service industry, but banned as a large scale paint stripper in many countries, construction; ship building and aircraft industries; food industry. |
| Diethyl sulphate | Alkylating agent in chemical synthesis. | Chemicals manufacturing. |
| N, N-dimethyl acetamide | Intermediate for manufacturing man made fibres, some use as a fine chemical and possibly in electronics industry. | Chemicals and pharmaceuticals manufacturing. |
| N, N-dimethylaniline | Chemical intermediate for dyes and other chemicals. | Chemicals manufacturing. |
| Dimethyl formamide | Used as a solvent in polyacrylontrile production. Also used as a general solvent and may have some uses in coatings but will be declining. Laboratory uses. | Chemicals manufacturing. |
| Dimethyl sulphate | Methylating agent used in chemical industry. | Chemicals manufacturing. |
| Dinitro benzene (all isomers) | Chemical intermediate. | Chemicals manufacturing. |
| 1,4-dioxane (Dioxane ) | As a process solvent in the manufacture of dyes, lacquers and detergents. | Chemicals manufacturing. |
| Endosulfan (ISO) | Pesticide. | Agriculture. |
| Ethane-1, 2-diol (Ethylene glycol) | Anti- freeze, also used in manufacture of polyesters. | Chemicals manufacturing; automotive industries. |
| 2-ethoxy ethanol (Cellosolve) | Widely used as solvent for oils, greases and waxes. Some coatings applications. | Coatings manufacture; construction; wood working industries. |
| Ethyl benzene | Major use is in production of styrene by dehydrogenation of ethyl benzene. Also as a solvent for resins. | Chemicals manufacturing. |

| CHEMICAL | MAJOR INDUSTRIAL USES | INDUSTRIAL SECTOR |
|---|---|---|
| 4-ethyl morpholine (N-ethylmorpholine) | As a catalyst in the manufacture of urethane foams, intermediate in dyes, pharmaceuticals and rubber accelerators. Solvent for resins and oils. | Chemicals manufacturing. |
| 2-furaldehyde (Furfural) | As a solvent in petrochemical industry. Manufacture of furfural based resins. | Petrochemicals, resin, abrasive papers and brake lining manufacturing industries; foundries. |
| Heptan-2-one (Methyl pentyl ketone) | Solvent and chemical intermediate. | Chemicals manufacturing. |
| Heptan-3-one | Solvent for nitrocellulose and polyvinyl resins, epoxides, vinyl coatings, finishes and adhesives. Also used as an intermediate in organic synthesis and as food flavouring. | Chemicals and coatings manufacture. |
| Hexan-2-one | Solvent and chemical intermediate. | Chemical and surface coatings manufacturing. |
| Hydrazine | Used as oxygen 'scavenger' in boiler water in power stations. | Chemicals manufacturing and power generation industries. |
| 2-hydroxypropyl-acrylate | Used in the manufacture of paints and other surface coatings. | Plastics, coatings and chemicals manufacturing. |
| Iodomethane (Methyl iodide) | Methylating agent (introduces –CH3 group). | Chemicals manufacturing. |
| Malathion | Pesticide e.g. head lice etc. | Agriculture; beauty industry; hospitals. |
| Methanol (methyl alcohol) | Widely used as a solvent and in chemical synthesis. Sometimes as a fuel. | Chemicals manufacturing. |
| 2-methoxy ethanol | As a solvent in paints, printing inks and printing ink wash solutions. De-icing agent in jet fuels. | Ship building and repair; coatings manufacturing; construction and printing industries; air transportation sectors. |
| 2-methoxyethyl acetate (Ethylene glycol monomethyl ether acetate) | Used in coatings. | Coatings manufacturing; construction; ship building and refitting; furniture making sectors. |
| 1-methoxypropan-2-ol | Solvent for paints, lacquers, resins etc. | Coatings manufacturing; construction; printing, furniture making; ship building and repair; air craft and motor vehicle manufacturing. |
| 1-methoxypropyl acetate | Used in formulation of coatings, cleaners and printing inks etc. | Solvent/ coatings industry |
| Methylene bis (2-chloroaniline) (MbOCA | Used in manufacture of moulded polyurethane articles. | Chemical manufacturing. |
| 4, 4' methylene dianiline (MDA) | Used as an intermediate in epoxy resins. | Resins and chemicals manufacturing. |
| N-Methylaniline | Intermediate in production of dyes, herbicides and other chemicals. | Chemicals manufacturing. |
| 5-methylhexan-2-one | Used in high boiling point lacquer and intermediate for phenylene. | Chemicals manufacturing. |
| 4-methylpentan-2-one | Solvent in glues, paint cleaners, plastics, fats, oils and waxes. | Chemicals and coatings manufacturing; construction; ship building and repairing sectors. |
| 1-methyl-2-pyrollidone (N-methyl-2-pyrollidone) | Wide ranging solvent. Used in agrochemicals, pharmaceuticals, electronics. | Pharmaceuticals and chemical manufacturing; electronics industry. |
| Monochloroacetic acid | Used as a paint remover, resin modifier, chemical intermediate. | Chemicals and coatings manufacturing; construction; furniture making. |

| CHEMICAL | MAJOR INDUSTRIAL USES | INDUSTRIAL SECTOR |
|---|---|---|
| Nickel (inorganic) | Manufacture of nickel salts. Production of stainless steel, other alloys, electroplating, coinage, and alkaline batteries. | Metal finishing; chemicals and coating manufacture. |
| Nicotine | Anti-smoking patches etc. | Pharmaceuticals industry. |
| Nitrobenzene | Production of aniline. | Chemicals manufacturing. |
| Phenol | Used in the synthesis of a variety of chemicals, including phenolic resins, specialised paint strippers and disinfectants | Chemical and pharmaceuticals manufacturing. |
| Phorate (ISO) | Pesticide. | Agriculture. |
| Piperidine | The major industrial application of piperidine is for the production of dipiperidinyl dithiuram tetrasulfide, which is used as a rubber vulcanization accelerator. | Chemicals and rubber products manufacturing. |
| Poly chlorinated biphenyls (PCBs) | Class of compounds known as polychlorinated biphenyls – now no longer manufactured. Still occur in the environment due to historic uses. | Ships and heavy electrical gear dismantling. |
| Propan-1-ol (n-propanol or propyl alcohol) | Solvent for a variety of applications including resins, cellulose esters and in the pharmaceutical industry. | Chemicals and pharmaceuticals manufacturing. |
| Prop-2-yn-1-ol (Propynol) | Propynol has been used to prevent the hydrogen embrittlement of steel. It has also been employed as a corrosion inhibitor, a solvent for cellulose acetate, a stabiliser for chlorinated hydrocarbon formulations, an herbicide, a polishing agent in galvanotechnics, a soil fumigant, and as a chemical intermediate. | Chemicals manufacturing; metal treatment; construction and agriculture sectors. |
| Sodium azide | Used as a broad-spectrum biocide and a detonator for powerful explosives. Used in specialist anticorrosion solutions and in airbags /aircraft safety chutes. Extremely poisonous. | Chemicals and explosives manufacture ring; car and other automotives dismantling. |
| Sulfotep (ISO) | Pesticide. | Agriculture. |
| o-toluidine (2-amino toluene) | Intermediate in the manufacture of dyes and other chemicals. | Chemicals manufacturing. |
| 1,1,2,2- tetrabromoethane | As a solvent for fats, oils and waxes. Mercury substitute in gauges. | Chemicals and gauges manufacturing. |
| Tetrohydrofuran | Solvent in a variety of applications. | Chemicals manufacturing. |
| Thallium (soluble compounds) | Thallium sulphide used in semiconductors. | Electronics. |
| Toluene | As a solvent in many applications including glues, paints, resins, petrol. | Chemical processing, coatings manufacture; petrochemical industries. |
| 1,2,4-trichlorobenzene | Chemical intermediate. | Chemicals and agro-chemicals manufacturing. |
| Trichloroethylene | Solvent, widely used as a degreasant. | Chemicals manufacturing; engineering; electroplating. |
| Triethylamine | Used in organic synthesis and as a curing agent, hardening and corrosion inhibitor for polymers. | Chemicals manufacturing. |
| 2,4,6-trinitro toluene (TNT) | Constituent of some commercial and military explosives. No other uses are significant. | Explosives manufacturing; military; demolition work. |
| Xylene (mixed isomers) | Used as solvents – many applications in paint stripping, electroplating, rubber manufacture. | Chemicals and coatings manufacturing; engineering; construction; metal finishing. |

## CONCLUSION

A review of the contents of Tables 4.1 and 4.2 makes it clear that a significant number of occupational settings will present the potential for dermal exposure to chemicals and wet-work. Hazardous agents involved are numerous and they can be present in various forms including pure substances, preparations and process-generated substances. A recent survey by the Health and Safety Executive (HSE) suggests that 50% of workers consider that their skin comes into regular contact with chemicals. About two million, (6% of the working population), are concerned about the harm that might arise from the dermal contact. Occupations at risk will require exposure assessment and, where necessary, adequate exposure control measures to prevent or minimise skin and systemic diseases. Professional Journals such as Contact Dermatitis, Journal of Occupational Medicine, Journal of Investigative Dermatology, British Journal of Dermatology and American Journal of Industrial Medicine regularly publish case studies to illustrate work-related ill-health associated with dermal exposure to chemicals and wet-work.

## TEST YOUR KNOWLEDGE

1. List as many as you can of the substances, products and materials that are likely to cause contact dermatitis in construction industry or at your workplace.

2. Select three substances, products or materials from the list you prepared earlier and explain how the contacts (all routes of exposure) take place and what controls may be used for adequate control of exposure. Always remember, PPE is the last resort.

## FURTHER READING

**2007 TLVs and BEIs. American Congress of Governmental Industrial Hygiene Association (ACGIHA),** Cincinnati, USA. ISBN 978 8824 17 69 8.

**ABC of work related disorders: Occupational cancers.** CA Veys. British Medical Journal; 313 (1996): 615-619.

**Canadian Centre for Occupational Health and Safety.** www.ccohs.ca

**Condensed Handbook of Occupational Dermatology.** Editors: L Kanerva, P Elsner, JE Whalberg and HI Maibach. Springer-Verlag, Berlin, Germany. ISBN 3 540 44348 7.

**Contact allergy in male construction workers in Sao Paula, Brazil, 2000-2005.** MS Macedo, AOA Alchorne, EB Costa, FT Montesano. Contact Dermatitis; 56 (2007): 232-234.

**EH40: Workplace exposure limits (published annually).** Health and Safety Executive, London, UK.

**Hand Eczema (2nd Edition).** T Menne and HI Maibach, CRC Press, New York, USA. ISBN 0 8493 7355 7.

**Incidence by occupation and industry of work-related skin diseases in the United Kingdom, 1996-2001.** JC McDonald, MH Beck, Y Chen, NM Cherry. Occupational Medicine; 56 (2006): 398-405.

**Occupational Safety and Health Administration.** www.osha.gov

**Occupational Skin Disease.** RM Adams. WB Saunders Company, London, UK. ISBN 0 7216 7037 7.

**Pocket Guide to Chemical Hazards (2005).** National Institute for Occupational Safety and Health (NIOSH), Cincinnati, USA.

**Skin and Occupation.** HB Van der Walle and WP Piebenga. Centre of Skin and Occupation. Centre of Skin and Occupation, Arnhem, The Netherlands. Yamanouchi Europe.

**Textbook of Contact Dermatitis.** Editors: RJG Rycroft, T Menné, PJ Frosch, JP Lepoittevin. Springer-Verlag, Berlin, Germany. ISBN 3 540 66842 X.

**Surface and Dermal Monitoring for Toxic Exposures.** SA Ness. Van Nostrand Reinhold. New York, USA. ISBN 0 442 01465 1.

**Workplace Contact Dermatitis.** Workplace Safety and Insurance Board, Ontario, Canada. www.wsib.on.ca

# Part 2

# DERMAL EXPOSURE TO CHEMICALS AND THE LAW

Chapter 5

# Dermal Exposure Control and Regulatory Requirements

## INTRODUCTION

The regulatory requirements described in this Chapter are those applicable in Great Britain (GB). The principles underpinning these requirements also form the basis of regulations for chemical exposure control in Europe, North America and Australasia. The primary duties, (related to health and safety), of employers, employees, manufacturers, importers, suppliers and health and safety inspectors are laid down in the Health and Safety at Work etc Act. The Act places duty on every employer to ensure, so far as is *reasonably practicable*, the health, safety and welfare at work of all employees.

The Management of Health and Safety at Work Regulations require employers to carry out *suitable and sufficient* assessment of the risks faced by their employees at work and by other persons arising out of the work undertaken by the employer. The risk assessments must identify the measures, which need to be taken to comply with statutory health and safety duties. The regulations also lay down general duties relating to planning; organising; monitoring, including health surveillance; reviewing preventive measures; appointing competent persons; dealing with emergencies and providing employees with information, instruction and training. Several other regulations place specific duties on employers in relation to chemicals. The purpose of these duties is to ensure that employees' exposure (by all routes) to chemicals is either prevented or *adequately controlled*.

Some regulations place specific duties on manufacturers, importers and suppliers of chemicals, chemical products, preparations, pesticides, biocides, machinery and personal protective equipment (PPE). One of the primary requirements of these regulations is that manufacturers, importers and suppliers must provide adequate information to the users of their chemicals, products, preparations, equipment or machinery. Adequate information is needed to ensure that employers can use chemicals, machinery, products, PPE and other equipment at their workplace without serious risks to the health and safety of their employees, others and themselves.

This Chapter summarises the requirements and duties for dermal exposure control. The leading law, in GB, in this area is the Control of Substances Hazardous to Health Regulations (COSHH). The requirements of these regulations are applicable to all routes of exposure. The publication, "Control of substances hazardous to health (Fifth edition)" provides a comprehensive description of the regulations and its requirements. Readers in GB are advised to be familiar with these requirements.

Other regulations relevant to chemical exposure control include:

- The Control of Lead at Work Regulations.
- The Control of Asbestos Regulations.
- The Confined Spaces Regulations.
- The Ionising Radiations Regulations and
- The Workplace (Health, Safety and Welfare) Regulations.
- The Information and Consultation with Employees Regulations.
- Reporting of Injuries, Diseases, and Dangerous Occurrences Regulations.

## PRINCIPLES UNDERPINNING HEALTH AND SAFETY LAW

Employees' health, safety and welfare are protected by law. The overriding duty of an employer is to prevent employees being exposed to *hazardous substances*. To achieve this, it is necessary to assess the potential for exposure by different exposure pathways and consider what types of reasonable precautions could be applied for preventing or adequately controlling exposure.

The duties of employers do not end with the provision of engineering controls and PPE. They should establish administrative procedures and create an environment to ensure that control measures are properly applied or used and are not made less effective by incorrect work practices or by improper use.

In general terms, an employer's duties include:

- Making sure that the workplace is safe and without unacceptable risks to health, safety and welfare. Ultimately a court of law will decide what risk is unacceptable in a given scenario. The law does not seek to establish "zero risk" workplaces, but it requires the application of sensible risk management approaches. The principles underpinning sensible risk management and those factors contributing to bureaucratic back covering are described in Appendix 3;

- Ensuring plant and machinery are safe to use, operate and maintain;

- Ensuring that safe systems of work are put in place and followed;

- Ensuring products and substances are moved, stored, used and disposed of safely;

- Providing adequate welfare facilities;

- Providing employees with the information, instruction, training and supervision as necessary to protect the health and safety; and

- Consulting and taking into account the views of employees or their representatives on matters of health and safety at work.

Employees have legal duties and these can be summarised as follows:

- Taking reasonable care for their own health and safety and that of others who may be affected by the work undertaken;

- Co-operating with the employer on health and safety matters;

- Correctly using work items provided by the employer. These will include work systems, procedures, machinery, chemicals, PPE, welfare facilities and any other protective measures; and

- Not interfering with or misusing anything that is provided for protecting their health, safety and welfare.

## DERMAL EXPOSURE CONTROL

The COSHH regulations deal with **"substances hazardous to health"**, as defined in the regulations. They include hazardous chemicals and these can be found in various physical states. These are:

- Gases (e.g. chlorine).

- Liquids (e.g. organic solvents and shampoos).

- Solids (e.g. nickel in coins and chromium in cement).

- Fumes (e.g. copper fume and welding fume).

- Dusts (e.g. wood and cement dusts).

- Mists (e.g. hydrochloric acid mist and paint sprays).

Chemicals used at work can be found in various forms. These include:

(i)     Pure substances (e.g. xylene);

(ii)    Chemicals mixed together as preparations or products (e.g. paints and metal working fluids);

(iii)   By-products (e.g. hydrofluoric acid generated when PTFE-O rings are inadvertently burnt in the presence of water);

(iv)    Process-generated products (e.g. Nickel fume generated during welding);

(v)     Waste products (e.g. hydrogen sulphide released from sewage);

(vi)    Animal feeds;

(vii)   Cleaning and beauty products (e.g. floor and equipment cleaning products, shampoos and nail adhesives);

(viii)  Natural products (e.g. terpenes extracted from pine trees and natural rubber proteins released from single-use latex gloves).

## The COSHH Regulations and Dermal Exposure

### Requirements for Carrying out Work

An employer must not carry out any work, which can expose, by any route (dermal, inhalation, and ingestion), employees to substances hazardous to health, unless the employer has:

(a)     *Carried out a "**suitable and sufficient**" risk assessment of the health risks created by that work <u>and</u> identified the steps needed to comply with the regulations <u>and</u>....*

(b)     *... Implemented the steps identified.*

The step (a) must consider whether it is **reasonably practicable** to prevent dermal exposure. If prevention is not reasonably practicable, the step should identify how to ensure **adequate control** of dermal exposure.

### Risk Assessment

A risk assessment must take account of the following:

I.      *Hazardous properties of the chemical(s).* Information on these may be found in safety data sheets (sometimes called material safety data sheets). Useful indicators include hazard/safety signs and phrases, toxicological information and skin notation ('Sk'). Hazard identification methods are described in Chapter 7.

Chapter 5

Dermal Exposure Control and Regulatory Requirements

II. *Health effects caused by the chemical(s).* Information on health effects may be found in safety data sheets. Other information sources include: trade association publications; regulatory publications such as *approved codes of practice*, industry sector information sheets; workplace exposure limits booklets (e.g. EH40); COSHH Essentials and information listed in Tables 4.1 and 4.2 in Chapter 4 or similar information obtained from other sources.

III. *The routes, extent, frequency and duration of exposure.* The routes of exposure include dermal, inhalation and ingestion; the extent of exposure will inform how much exposure is taking place (e.g. minor, gross contamination); the frequency of exposure will identify how often the exposure is taking place (e.g. daily, weekly, intermittently during the day, accidental); duration of exposure will identify how long the exposure is taking place (e.g. minutes, hours);

IV. *Amount of chemical(s) used or produced.* For example, those produced intentionally, others produced as by-products, released by chemical reactions during the process or found in waste products.

V. *Type of work* (e.g. emergency, maintenance or routine work). Where it is carried out (e.g. fixed installation, temporary site or a peripatetic work).

VI. *The effectiveness of controls.* The expected effectiveness of the control steps identified, as needed, during the risk assessment or existing preventive/control measures.

VII. *The results of any monitoring data* (e.g. surface contamination, skin contamination and biological monitoring).

VIII. *The results of applicable health surveillance data.* For example, information obtained during skin inspection and skin condition monitoring; workplace information on incidence or prevalence rates of dermatitis and other types of skin disease.

**Recording a Risk Assessment**

Where there are 5 or more employees, the employer must record the findings of:

(a) The risk assessment and

(b) The preventive or control steps to be put in place to comply with the regulations.

**Reviewing a Risk Assessment**

The employer must review the assessment if:

*(a)* For any reason, the assessment is considered to be not valid (e.g. the chemical composition of the product has changed), or

*(b)* The work has changed and it has no resemblance to the assessment in place (e.g. the rate of production has reduced significantly), or

*(c)* Other information has become available and indicates that the assessment is no longer valid (e.g. information provided on current safety data sheet; outbreak of dermatitis in the workplace or elsewhere and reported or known widely; dermal, surface or biological exposure monitoring results indicates that exposure is not under control).

**Adequate Control of Dermal Exposure**

The employer must consider and apply, as appropriate for the circumstances of the work, the "principles of good control practice". Their application is necessary for achieving adequate dermal exposure control and will include all of the following:

I. Designing and operating processes, tasks and activities to minimise emission, release and spread of chemicals.

II. Taking account of relevant routes of exposure including surface contamination and skin exposure that has already taken place and their potential for contributing to ingestion and inhalation. For example, contaminated fingers may be placed in the nose area resulting in inhalation exposure; contaminated fingers may be used for consuming food; contamination released from coveralls may be inhaled. These types of inadvertent exposures are often missed by inhalation exposure monitoring methods and mechanical control measures. These types of exposures could lead to a significant body burden and disease.

III. Controlling exposure by measures that are proportionate to the health risk.

IV. Choosing the most effective and reliable control options. These will include the application of safe working distance (SWD) approach to process, product design and handling methods. Control measures applied should minimise the escape and spread of chemicals and deliver adequate control. For example, local exhaust ventilation (LEV) design should take account of ergonomics, and the need to minimise dermal exposure. Examples of practical control measures are described in Part 4.

V. Providing suitable PPE, skin care products and washing facilities.

VI. Carrying out supervision, monitoring, checks, maintenance and regular review of all control measures. These are needed to ensure that all elements of control measures remain effective.

VII. Providing information, instruction and training (IIT) to employees. IIT should cover dermal exposure and the risks arising from the use of chemicals and how to correctly use all types of control measures, including PPE and skin care products. The IIT should include information on the limitations of control measures and the consequences of failure to correctly use the control measures. IIT should consider key communication factors described in Chapter 14.

VIII. Ensuring control measures put in place do not increase the overall risks to health and safety. For example, installing and using a centrifugal fan in a local exhaust ventilation system designed to deal with highly flammable materials can increase the risk of fire and explosion. A suitable fan would be a bifurcated type.

## CONCLUSION

This Chapter provides a concise explanation of the requirements of COSHH regulations. It would require a separate book to explain every aspect of the law. This is already available in the form of "Control of substances hazardous to health (Fifth edition)", which includes the approved code of practice and guidance on the regulations. The requirements and procedures for achieving adequate control will vary according to the nature of work, the chemicals used, the extent of exposure, the workers involved and the associated health and safety risks. Practical dermal exposure control issues are described in Part 4 of this book. In a practical book like this, it would be impossible to discuss every chemical regulation enacted in the UK and elsewhere in the World. It is anticipated that readers will seek out relevant regulations that are applicable to a given situation. Where wet-work does not involve hazardous chemicals, the requirement for adequate control of the risks will be subjected to the Health and Safety at Work etc Act and The Management of Health and Safety at Work Regulations.

## TEST YOUR KNOWLEDGE

1. What are the principles underpinning health and safety regulations worldwide?

2. What are the key tests of the risk assessment that must be satisfied before carrying out work with chemicals, under the COSHH regulations?

3. What factors should be taken into account when carrying out a suitable and sufficient assessment for dermal exposure control?

4. List the eight "principles of good control practice" and assess a task at your workplace to establish whether it complies with the requirements.

5. Select two of the principles of good control practice and examine how you would apply them to dermal exposure control requirements at your workplace.

## FURTHER READING

**Chemicals (Hazard Information) and Packaging for Supply Regulations 2002.** Redgrave's Health and Safety (fifth edition). Michael Ford. Butterworths LexisNexis, London, UK. ISBN 0 406 95813 0.

**Code of Federal Regulations 29 CFR 1910: Occupational Safety and Health Standards.** Toxic and Hazardous Substances. Occupational Safety and Health Administration, Washington, USA.

**Code of Practice: Code of practice for the control of workplace hazardous substances.** WorkCover Authority, New South Wales, Australia.

**Control of Exposure to Biological and Chemical Agents. Regulations 833 – as amended.** Canadian Centre for Occupational Health and Safety. Ontario, Canada.

**Control of substances hazardous to health (Fifth edition).** HSE Books, Sudbury, UK. ISBN 0 7176 2981 3.

**EH40/2005 Workplace exposure limits.** HSE Books, Sudbury, UK. ISBN 0 7176 2977 5.

**Enforcement policy statement (HSC15).** HSE Books, Sudbury, UK.

**Framework Directive (89/391/EEC).** The European Commission, Brussels, Belgium.

**Health and Safety Law. What you should know.** HSE Books, Sudbury, UK.

**Health and safety (consultation with employees) Regulations 1996.** Redgrave's Health and Safety (fifth edition). Michael Ford. Butterworths LexisNexis. London, UK. ISBN 0 406 95813 0.

**Health and Safety at Work etc Act 1974.** Redgrave's Health and Safety (fifth edition). Michael Ford. Butterworths LexisNexis, London, UK. ISBN 0 406 95813 0.

**Principles of sensible risk management.** http://www.hse.gov.uk/risk

**Reporting of Injuries, Diseases and Dangerous Occurrences Regulations 1995.** Redgrave's Health and Safety (fifth edition). Michael Ford. Butterworths LexisNexis, London, UK. ISBN 0 406 95813 0.

**Safe work in confined spaces, The Confined Spaces Regulation 1997,** Health and Safety Executive, London, UK. ISBN 0-7176-1405-0.

**The Control of Lead at Work Regulations.** Health and Safety Executive, London, UK. ISBN 0 11 04 2917 6.

**The Ionising Radiations Regulations 1999.** Statutory Instrument 1999, number 3232. HM Stationary Office, London, UK.

**The Chemical Agents Directive, 98/24/EC.** Official Journal of the European Communities. L131/11/5.5.98.

# Part 3

# DERMAL EXPOSURE HAZARD AND RISK IDENTIFICATION

*Chapter 6*

# Dermal Exposure Pathways

## INTRODUCTION

Workplace exposure to chemical substances, products and materials may occur as a result of dermal contact, inhalation and/or ingestion. Severe skin diseases, poisoning and multiple fatalities due to dermal exposure to chemicals have been reported over several decades. Contact dermatitis accounts for about 80% of occupational skin disease. Approximately, 80% work-related contact dermatitis is to the hands. Apart from chemicals, *wet-work* is a significant contributor to irritant contact dermatitis.

Despite this evidence, the need for an understanding of dermal exposure pathways and the development of practical dermal exposure control strategies (i.e. exposure risk assessment, exposure measurement methods and exposure control approaches) remain a low priority among many health and safety specialists. Efforts are mainly focussed on inhalation exposure, because it is considered to be the important route of exposure. There is still a belief that using personal protective equipment (PPE) is the way to control dermal exposure. Fortunately, these attitudes are rapidly changing with widespread recognition that dermal exposure to chemicals and wet-work leads to a significant burden of work-related ill health as explained in Chapter 3. Because of this recognition, a number of agencies, in many parts of the world, are devoting resources to understand how dermal exposure occurs and for developing suitable dermal exposure measurement and control techniques.

In this Chapter, a practical description of dermal exposure pathways is given. This will provide a basis for the control approaches described in Part 4 of this book.

## WHAT IS MEANT BY DERMAL EXPOSURE?

Dermal exposure may be described as the amount of *hazardous substance* contacted by the outer layer (horny layer) of the skin and being available for dermal uptake (absorption) via the unbroken skin and/or for producing an effect on the skin. The effect on the skin may be at the point of contact or elsewhere.

## DYNAMICS OF DERMAL EXPOSURE

There seems to be a view that assessing dermal exposure is a complex task and will always require an expert such as an occupational hygienist. If the dermal exposure pathways are explained in a simple and practical way it should not be the case in every circumstance. This approach should enable "*frontline*" personnel to implement dermal exposure control measures in the majority of circumstances.

To achieve this aim, it is necessary to appreciate and take account of the dynamic interaction between the skin and hazardous substances present in the immediate environment surrounding the skin surface. Skin comes into contact with contaminants arising from different sources, which include:

● Air close to the skin;

● The product being used, worked on or produced. For example, products used during brick laying include wet cement and sand;

● Contaminated surfaces. These will include surfaces of product containers, workbenches, work tools, cleaning equipment, ventilation hoods, dust collection bags and many other surfaces;

● Contaminated PPE, such as gloves, coveralls and footwear;

● Contaminated street clothing.

The process of transferring contamination to the skin is somewhat different from inhalation exposure because the contaminants may move to and from the skin. In other words, the transfer process is multidirectional and dynamic. During this dynamic process, a contaminant may move from the skin to air, clothing and work surfaces. Some, or all of it, may return to the skin from various sources as described above. Contaminants may move from work surfaces to PPE and air. From these sources it may reach the skin. Similarly, it may move from work tools to air and then to the skin, and so on.

Furthermore, a contaminant may escape rapidly from the skin surface without being a significant contributor to the effects on the skin or elsewhere in the body. This can happen due to evaporation or some other action like wiping or washing.

Figure 6.1 can be used to illustrate the multidirectional process. This picture was taken at a cable manufacturing company. It shows that dermal exposure to the dust arose from multiple sources (e.g. dust in the air, PPE, floor, process equipment and clothing). The dust reaching the skin can move away from the skin in multiple directions, such as, to the surrounding air, clothing and footwear. In this particular situation, the process design and the work practices show that it can be difficult to make reliable and highly reproducible quantitative measurements of dermal exposure. However, it will become clearer that it is not necessary to obtain highly reliable quantitative exposure data on every occasion, to achieve adequate control of dermal exposure.

**Figure 6.1**

**Skin exposure resulting from multiple sources**.
In this process, a dusty material is being applied to the cable to stop it sticking after it has been wound to a reel. Dust from a number of sources - turntables, gloves, clothing, footwear, other equipment and contaminated floor- can contaminate the skin. Dust on the skin can be retained or lost. Some may return to the skin through contact with contaminated surfaces.

## DERMAL EXPOSURE PATHWAYS

In general, occupational hygienists place dermal exposure pathways in four key categories.

- Direct contact including immersion,
- Deposition from air,
- Splashing and
- Surface contact.

However, for the purposes of practical dermal exposure risk assessment and control, these dermal exposure pathways are expanded and explained in the following manner.

- **Direct contact with hands** - Skin contact takes place when hands are intentionally used as a tool for handling or manipulating chemicals or chemical-containing materials, tools and equipment. For example, handling a bolus of rubber in toluene as shown in Figure 6.2

- **Immersion (hands)** - Skin contact takes place when hands, sometimes hands and forearms, are immersed in a chemical substance or a product. An example is illustrated in Figure 6.3.

- **Direct contact with other parts of the body** - Skin surface other than the areas of the hands, can come into direct contact with contaminants due to the way the work is carried out (Figure 6.4). Figure 2.2 shows serious burns to the knee of a floor layer caused by wet cement.

- **Deposition** - This can happen when airborne contaminants impact or settle on the skin (Figure 6.5). Contaminants can be in the form of gas/vapour, dust, fibre, fume, or liquid mist. Figure 2.3 shows how quickly vapours in air can be absorbed through an unbroken skin.

- **Contact with surfaces** - The skin often comes into contact with contaminated work surfaces. The potential is shown in Figure 6.6.

- **Contact with contaminated clothing and or PPE** - it will provide ample opportunities for the skin to come into contact with chemicals. An example is shown in Figure 6.7.

- **Splashing -** Splashes can land on the skin or clothing. This takes place when liquids, liquid based mixes or powders are involved. Careless or inappropriate handling of liquids or liquid mixes, as shown in Figure 6.8, can cause splashing to occur. Solvents coming into contact with clothing may produce a vapour cloud in the breathing zone of the person leading to inadvertent inhalation exposure; may be absorbed via the skin; or may cause damage to the surface of the skin.

Dermal exposure through these seven inter-related pathways would not take place in isolation. In practice, and in most cases, many of these pathways will be contributing simultaneously to skin exposure as shown in Figure 6.5. The examples, described in this Chapter, show that it is often simple to determine dermal exposure pathways and estimate the likely exposure levels. The identification of the dermal exposure pathways will provide ideas for the development of suitable control strategies.

**Figure 6.2 – Direct contact with hands**.

In this task, rubber dough, (made by mixing rubber granules and a purple colour dye in toluene), is being made into a 'ball' for placing close to the coating knife in the fabric coating machine. There is a red solvent can on a sheet of paper in the foreground.

The process operators use toluene from the can to clean excess rubber mix on hands. The paper is used to soak up spills. Exposure to toluene can damage the 'bricks and mortar' like arrangement of the horny layer leading to irritant contact dermatitis and can enhance uptake of toluene via the skin, which can cause damage to other parts of the body.

*(Note: it is practicable to prevent skin exposure by using simple semi automated delivery systems; the 'Elephant-trunk' LEV system is ineffective for exposure control but has an unwanted effect - expelling heated air.)*

**Figure 6.3 – Immersion**.

In this case, a potter is using his hands as a tool to glaze pots. His hands and footwear are contaminated with the glaze. Secondary contamination of the hands can take place when they come into contact with contaminated footwear and other surfaces.

It is practicable to perform this work using a simple 'S' hook – to dip, drain excess glaze and transport the items to a curing oven.

**Figure 6.4 – Direct contact with body parts**.

An 'elephant-trunk' hose discharging the wet-cement is being held under the arm pits. Contamination on the hose can cause skin exposure. In addition, there is exposure to UV radiation from the sun.

Damages caused by wet cement are shown in figs 2.2 and 3.7.

**Figure 6.5 – Deposition from air**.

This operator is working within a dust cloud, leading to skin and inhalation exposure. The dust settling on clothing, work surfaces and work-pieces can contribute to skin and inadvertent inhalation exposure as well as ingestion.

Contaminated street clothing can transport chemicals to other places creating a potential for third party exposures.

**Figure 6.6 – Contact with surfaces**.

In this case, a sticky but very toxic substance, methylene bis 2-chloroaniline (MbCOA), was transferred to surfaces, including drinking mugs, in the 'amenity' area.

The contamination was brought to this area, by workers (unintentionally and unseen), on surfaces such as hands and clothing.

This picture is showing a substandard welfare facility (see Chapters 5 and 12). The brown stain on the wall was caused by the action of throwing away used tea bags and left-over drinks.

**Figure 6.7 – Contact with clothing and personal protective equipment (PPE)**.

Special lighting makes mist visible

This picture is showing paint (isocyanate containing) being sprayed. Part of the over-spray (fine aerosols) can land on the coverall, gloves and visor worn by the operator. If the contaminated PPE is removed without careful attention, hands and other parts of the body can become contaminated. Skin and inhalation exposure to isocyanates has the potential to cause respiratory sensitisation.

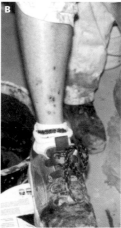

**Figure 6.8 – Splashing**.

(A) Splashing can take place during loading and mixing. The areas around the mixing container and the coverall are heavily contaminated with dust. These can contribute to skin and inhalation exposure.

(B) Epoxy resin-related allergic contact dermatitis had been caused by resins coming into contact with legs through contaminated coveralls.

*Photographs: Courtesy of the European Epoxy Project Team and IVAM, Amsterdam, The Netherlands. Another example of ACD is in fig 2.4.*

## DERMAL EXPOSURE AND THE BODY

### Hands and Contamination

When a work task is being executed, various parts of the human body perform a number of complex functions. The hands are often used as work tools for accomplishing tasks. Workers often immerse their hands in chemicals and this action can take place without any consideration of the consequences resulting from that exposure. As an example, a construction worker may allow without any intention his/her skin to become exposed to wet cement. This exposure presents a significant potential for "cement burns", irritant and allergic contact dermatitis. It is clear that preventing chemical and wet-work exposure to the hands should be the priority. This will lead to significant reductions in work-related contact dermatitis and systemic disease resulting from dermal absorption.

### Inadvertent Exposures Resulting from Skin and Surface Contamination

Workers, third parties at work and those away from workplaces can receive inadvertent inhalation, ingestion and skin exposures as a result of contaminated skin and surfaces. Sources contributing to these exposures include:

- Contaminated hands - These may be placed on the skin area close to the nostrils leading to inhalation exposure immediately after the contact or over a period of time. A number of chemicals and products (e.g. phenol, different types of amines and dusts) could be inhaled in significant quantities in this way.

- Contaminated glove - If placed close to the nostrils, it may cause inadvertent inhalation exposure to chemicals. This can happen when wiping or blowing the nose. In some occasions, a contaminated glove can cause exposure to other parts of the body. It is possible that someone will store chemically contaminated gloves in a trouser pocket. Chemicals on the glove can then reach the skin area on the thigh and may cause effects on the skin or elsewhere in the body, if absorbed in sufficient quantities. Third parties at work may become exposed to chemicals on contaminated gloves. A dirty glove may contaminate surfaces such as paperwork used for process management.

- Contaminated coveralls - These are potential sources for significant inadvertent inhalation exposure. This potential is clearly demonstrated in Figure 2.5. On the other hand, if this coverall was taken home, family members could be exposed to hazardous substances. Employers should consider these factors, especially when they have peripatetic workers who will go home directly from their temporary workplaces. Coveralls and other clothing can absorb organic substances including solvents. This situation can create a resident

vapour cloud in the close vicinity of the worker, contributing to inhalation exposure and dermal uptake (see Figure 2.4).

- Contaminated street clothing - Some workers may wear street clothing whilst working with hazardous substances. These clothes when contaminated, can act as potential sources for inadvertent inhalation exposure. Recently, the UK Ministry of Defence accepted liability for third party mesothelioma caused by inadvertent inhalation exposure. The exposure to a family member (third party outside work) took place in the worker's home because the victim's father (the worker) brought home asbestos fibres on his clothing without him realising that this might happen.

- Contaminated footwear - They can act as a reservoir for contamination. When the contaminated footwear is removed, hands may become contaminated. Contaminated hands can be placed close to the nostrils leading to inadvertent inhalation exposure. The same contaminated hands may also be used for consuming food leading to ingestion of toxic chemicals.

- Contaminated surfaces - Exposure can happen in many ways. For example, by touching contaminated surfaces such as portable ventilation hoods and their pipe work; work pieces; tools; and rest room furniture or elsewhere (e.g. contaminated surfaces in a car boot). Contaminated surfaces can create dust and vapour clouds invisible to the naked eye. Operators and third parties at work could be exposed to these.

The majority of inadvertent exposures are likely to be missed by regular inhalation and dermal exposure monitoring regimes. These exposures may take place when the samplers are not located on the person. This fact should be considered when interpreting exposure measurement results. Often assessments do not consider the potential for inadvertent exposures, whether it is inhalation, dermal or ingestion.

## A LACK OF FOCUS ON DERMAL EXPOSURE

Until recently, the main focus of chemical exposure risk control was on inhalation. There are many reasons for this, which include:

- Skin exposure is considered as "part of the job".

- A lack of understanding that many substances can easily pass through the skin leading to over estimation of the skin as a barrier.

- Other exposure routes were not considered as significant as the inhalation route.

- Availability and use of PPE, skin care products and washing facilities have been considered as the main answer to dermal exposure control.

- Regulations may not have given a balanced attention to the health risks arising from dermal exposure, especially when the health effects are on the skin.

- Enforcers' inattention or a significantly reduced focus on matters relating to adequate control of dermal exposure including the need to apply adequate safe working distance (SWD).

- Lack of suitable and readily available practical workbook type reference sources on dermal exposure assessment, exposure monitoring and control.

- Many of the dermal exposure monitoring methods are either in their infancy or are expensive and complicated for practical use in the workplace.

- Many monitoring methods suffer from significant uncertainties and this was thought to be a problem. It should be borne in mind that semi-quantitative and qualitative measurements have a useful role in dermal exposure risk management.

- It can be difficult to interpret the monitoring results. In other words, considerable expertise is needed to make any sense of quantitative exposure data.

- The validity and applicability of quantitative dermal exposure data may be vigorously challenged, unless they are backed up by practical standards and quality assurance programmes.

- There are no legally binding exposure standards for comparison. It is unlikely that legally binding dermal occupational exposure limits (DOEL) will be developed in the short to medium term. However, values for 'total daily dermal contamination giving cause for concern" has been suggested by the Health and Safety Executive (HSE) and these values are useful for dermal exposure risk management including monitoring. These values are listed in Table 8.2 in Chapter 8.

## CONCLUSION

The approach taken to explain dermal exposure pathways should go a long way to making it easy to understand. Illustrations and examples used throughout this book should help to enhance that understanding. They should also be useful for training, instruction and for developing and implementing practical dermal exposure control measures.

Dermal exposure to chemical agents and the resulting health effects are receiving greater attention from researchers, legislators and employers. This attention is leading to regulatory initiatives and new approaches to the design of products and processes. Simple qualitative dermal and surface contamination monitoring methods are available for day-to-day applications and these are described in Chapter 8. There is an increasing use of non-invasive biological and skin monitoring methods to aid decision making. New initiatives in the areas of legislation, exposure assessment and control strategies should go a long way to reducing work-related skin and systemic diseases arising from dermal exposure to chemicals and wet-work.

## TEST YOUR KNOWLEDGE

1. List potential dermal exposure pathways and explain how contaminants come into contact with the skin.

2. Give reasons for the statement, "The hands are the most contaminated part of the body".

3. Explain why dermal exposure to chemicals and chemically contaminated clothing and PPE can contribute to inadvertent inhalation exposure and ingestion.

4. Why do you think there may be a lack of focus on dermal exposure control?

## FURTHER READING

**A critique of assumptions about selecting chemical-resistant gloves: A case for workplace evaluation of glove efficiency.** TD Klingner and MF Boeniger. Applied Occupational and Environmental Hygiene; 17 (2002): 360-367.

**Assessing and managing risks at work from skin exposure to chemical agents.** HSG205. HSE Books, Sudbury, UK. ISBN  0 7176 1826 9.

**Conceptual model for assessment of dermal exposure.** T Schneider, R Vermeulen, DH Brouwer, JW Cherrie, H Kromhout and CL Fogh. Occupational and Environmental Medicine; 56 (1999): 765-773.

**Control of Substances Hazardous to Health (Fifth edition) L5.** HSE Books, Sudbury, UK. ISBN 9 780717 629817.

**Dermal exposure: a decade of real progress.** RA Fenske. Annals of Occupational Hygiene; 44 (2000): 489-491.

**Dermal exposure assessment.** T Schneider, JW Cherrie, R Vermeulen and H Kromhout. Annals of Occupational Hygiene; 44 (2000): 493-499.

**Patterns of dermal exposure to hazardous substances in European Union workplaces.** R Rajan-Sithamparanadarajah, M Roff, P Delgado et al., Annals of Occupational Hygiene; 48 (2004): 285-297.

**Rash Decisions.** HSE Video, HSE Books, Sudbury, UK.

**Risks and possibilities in patch testing with contaminated personal objects: usefulness of thinlayer chromatograms in a patient with acrylate contact allergy from a chemical burn.** M Isaksson and E Zimerson. Contact Dermatitis; 57 (2007): 84-88.

# *Chapter 7*

# Dermal Hazard
# Identification Methods

## INTRODUCTION

There are suggestions that dermal exposure risk assessment and dermal exposure risk management (DERM) are complex tasks. These suggestions present a challenge because many workplaces, where chemical exposure and wet-work is an issue, are small and medium sized (SMEs) enterprises. A large majority of these do not employ dedicated health and safety professionals. In addition, many *frontline* health and safety professionals do not possess expert knowledge in occupational hygiene, toxicology or medicine.

This Chapter and the Chapters following are aimed at providing simplified approaches to DERM. It is hoped that these approaches will help to increase awareness (and competency) of dermal exposure control issues among health and safety professionals and trades unions health and safety representatives. In turn, it is hoped that this will benefit SMEs.

DERM should be based on "sensible risk management" principles (as described in Appendix 3) leading to the identification of significant dermal exposure risks and the necessary steps for adequate dermal exposure control. In this Chapter, some hazard identification methods are explained.

## DERMAL EXPOSURE LIMITS

Unlike inhalation exposure, there are no occupational exposure limits for dermal exposure. There are many practical difficulties preventing the development and use of legally binding DOELs (dermal occupational exposure limits). These include the need for establishing internationally acceptable limits for 'no observed adverse effect level' for dermal uptake and for effects on the skin. It is unlikely that DOELs will be set in the short to medium term.

The absence of DOELs is not an impediment to the identification of dermal hazards, exposure monitoring or

dermal exposure risk management. There are several helpful approaches that can be used effectively. Many of these are described below.

## CHEMICAL HAZARD INFORMATION AND LABELLING

Legal requirements for chemicals hazard information and labelling are in operation throughout the World, with minor variations between countries. Recently, the United Nations has taken a positive step to bring about a globally harmonised system (GHS) for classification and labelling of chemicals. It is hoped that in time this will be adopted by all member states. The European Union has developed the Registration, Evaluation and Assessment of Chemicals (REACH) regulations, which takes account of the GHS system.

### Chemicals (Hazard Information and Packaging for Supply) Regulations (CHIP)

These regulations apply to the supply of "chemicals" in the UK. In this context, "chemicals" mean single hazardous substances (e.g. acetone), preparations (e.g. paint strippers) and products (e.g. epoxy resins). Supply means selling, providing commercial samples or transferring chemicals from one person to another.

The supplier of a chemical must decide whether the chemical offered is hazardous. To do this they would follow the rules in CHIP and the Approved Classification and Labelling Guide. Many commonly used chemicals (in the region of 10,000) have already been classified and appear in the CHIP Approved Supply List. If the product supplied contains a mixture of hazardous substances, then the supplier must classify the product taking account of the hazardous properties of the individual chemical substances making up the product. For example, products such as paints, epoxy resins, metal working fluids, print blanket wash solvents and floor cleaning fluids are mixtures and will fall into this category.

A supplier of a classified hazardous chemical must

provide information for hazard identification and risk control. The types of information provided by the supplier will include:

● Hazard phrase(s);

● Hazard signs;

● Safety Phrase(s);

● Safety data sheet (Material Hazard Data Sheet); and

● Label.

However, several researchers have found that many manufacturers are failing to classify their products correctly, particularly in Safety Data Sheets (SDS). For example, when a sample of 19 SDSs, for two-part motor vehicle paints, was analysed, over 45% failed to document that the paints contained a respiratory sensitiser - isocyanate. Some manufacturers are failing to warn users that certain products may generate hazardous substances when they are put to use. For example, some metal working fluids may contain paraformaldehyde as a biocide. This will decompose to generate formaldehyde during use (i.e. when the working solution is made up with water). Formaldehyde is a skin sensitiser and there is limited evidence to suggest that it could cause cancer. One way to ensure that employers have got the right information to discharge their legal responsibilities is to write to the supplier of the product and seek confirmation

that they have provided all the necessary information. A sample letter in Figure 7.1 may be used for this purpose.

If a company produces a chemical for use in-house to manufacture another chemical, the company should decide whether the chemical produced is hazardous or not. If it is hazardous, the company must derive hazard and safety phrases, allocate appropriate hazard signs and prepare a suitable label and SDS.

**What is not covered by CHIP?**

The CHIP regulations do not apply to chemicals like medicines, cosmetics and process-generated substances (e.g. welding fume; dust and vapours released from medium density fibreboard; and natural products such as wood and sand). However, these materials can cause diseases resulting from inhalation and dermal exposure. It is well known that the abrasive action caused by wood chipping and sand can cause irritant contact dermatitis. Some types of wood dust may cause skin and respiratory sensitisation. Medium density fibreboard has the potential to release formaldehyde. When substances not covered by the CHIP regulations are used, it is always prudent to consult and get help from the trade association relevant to the business. Alternatively, publications of regulatory authorities should provide help.

Dear Sir/Madam

Re: *name of the product*

**Health and Safety at work etc Act., Chemicals (hazard Information and Packaging for Supply) Regulations, The Management of health and Safety at Work Regulations and the Control of Substances Hazardous to Health Regulations**

We are using your product *xxx* in our *yyy* process or task. We have a copy of your Safety Data Sheet (SDS) for the product. In order to undertake a suitable and sufficient health risk assessment, under the above regulations, we need to be sure that the information provided in your SDS is current and up-to-date.

In particular, we need to know whether the product contains any carcinogens (R40), respiratory (R42) or skin sensitisers (R43) at levels below the legally permitted minimum for the purpose of product classification. In addition, we want to know whether the product contains substances that may decompose in some way to release active chemicals during use in our process (for example, you may be aware that, some metal working fluids contain paraformaldehyde, which releases formaldehyde during use). We use your product in the following processes:

............................................................... (Note: describe the process)

Could you please confirm that the hazard, safety and chemical constitution information is current and up-to-date as described in your SDS (a copy is attached).

We anticipate that you will provide the necessary information within a week.

**Figure 7.1:** A sample letter to suppliers of chemicals and preparations

## HAZARD IDENTIFICATION METHODS

### Hazard phrases

These provide information on physical (e.g. explosive hazard), health and environmental hazards associated with chemicals. The CHIP regulations require that chemicals hazard information is communicated using "risk phrases". These phrases are denoted by the prefix R and followed by the relevant hazard number (e.g. R43 – may cause sensitisation by skin contact). The approach is similar to the GHS system. Hazard phrases help to convey the message that the chemical in question has the potential to cause harm. They do not go beyond that. They do not inform whether the potential identified will be realised in a particular work situation and will result in harm or the extent of that harm. These are answered by the risk assessment required by law and which should be carried out by the employer.

One or more of the following hazard phrases apply to chemicals having the potential to cause health effects on the skin.

- R34 - causes burns
- R35 - causes severe burns
- R36 - irritating to the eyes
- R38 - irritating to the skin
- R43 - may cause sensitisation by skin contact
- R66 - repeated exposure may cause skin dryness or cracking

One or more of the following hazard phrases apply to chemicals which have the potential to cause health effects elsewhere in the body as a result of dermal exposure.

- R21 - harmful in contact with the skin
- R24 - toxic in contact with the skin
- R27 - very toxic in contact with the skin
- R20/21 - harmful by inhalation and in contact with skin
- R39/24 - toxic, danger of very serious irreversible effects in contact with skin
- R39/27 - very toxic, danger of very serious irreversible effects in contact with skin
- R48/21 - harmful, danger of serious damage to health by prolonged exposure in contact with skin
- R48/24 - toxic, danger of serious damage to health by prolonged exposure in contact with skin
- R68/21 - harmful, possible risk of irreversible effects in contact with skin

### Labels

Containers and packages of hazardous chemicals must be labelled. The purpose of the label is to provide visual and written information on hazards and brief advice on what precautions should be taken to minimise risks. If the chemical is supplied from a tanker or down a pipeline it may not be labelled in accordance with the CHIP regulations. In such cases, safety data sheets are the key and the user of the chemical may then mark the container or the pipeline servicing the delivered chemical.

The following labelling signs should help to identify relevance to dermal exposure.

- Very toxic. These chemicals at very low levels can cause damage to health.
- Toxic. These chemicals at low levels can cause damage to health.
- Harmful. These chemicals may cause damage to health.
- Irritant. These chemicals may cause inflammation to the skin or other mucous membranes.
- Corrosive. These chemicals may destroy living tissues on contact.

### Safety Phrases

The purpose of safety phrases is to give information about the kind of precautions needed to prevent or control exposure or what to do in the event of an exposure or accident happening. Safety phrases are useful for dermal exposure risk assessment. The information provided by a safety phrase should be taken into account and integrated into control solutions. The following safety phrases are most relevant to dermal exposure assessment and control.

- S20 - when using do not eat or drink
- S21 - when using do not smoke
- S24 - avoid contact with skin
- S25 - avoid contact with eyes
- S26 - in case of contact with eyes, rinse immediately with plenty of water and seek medical advice
- S27 - take off immediately all contaminated clothing
- S28 - after contact with skin, wash immediately with plenty of …… (as specified by the manufacturer)
- S36 - wear suitable protective clothing
- S37 - wear suitable gloves
- S39 - wear suitable eye and face protection

## Safety data sheets

Safety data sheets (SDSs) are an important and vital resource for hazard identification and exposure control decisions. They should provide information about hazardous properties, potential health and safety risks and recommendation on handling, storage and waste disposal of chemicals. However, suppliers of "chemical preparations" (e.g. paints, metal working fluids, printing inks) are not required to list substances which are present at concentrations below a cut-off level (e.g. less than 1% in certain preparations). Where it is considered that the information provided in a safety data sheet is unhelpful or unclear, always write to the supplier and seek clarification. The sample letter in Figure 7.1 or similar is a useful check for ensuring that the supplier has given relevant information. Additional help may be available from the trade association relevant to the sector.

## Skin Notation

A number of substances carry a skin notation (e.g. 'Sk'-GB; 'Abs' - USA) and are indicated in publications such as EH40 - workplace exposure limits published by the Health and Safety Executive (HSE), and Threshold Limit Values (TLV) published by the American Conference of Governmental Industrial Hygienists (ACGIH) and the National Institute of Occupational Safety and Health (NIOSH). The purpose of this notation is to warn users that the substance can contribute significantly to the total body burden by uptake via the unbroken skin and may cause serious health effects elsewhere in the body. The 'Skin' notation is a qualitative indicator and is very useful for dermal exposure risk assessment and control. Manufacturers of chemicals may not allocate or provide a 'Skin' notation for their products, as this is not required by law. In addition, the approaches used for assigning 'Skin' notation vary from one country to another.

EH40 lists 88 substances in this category. However, there are other substances that have the potential to pass thorough the unbroken skin, but have not attracted the 'Sk' notation in GB. Many of these chemicals have been assigned the 'Skin' notation in other countries such as Germany and USA. When undertaking an assessment, 'Skin' notation should be used in conjunction with hazard and safety phrases. The publications cited above and the information provided in Table 4.2 should be useful for the purpose.

## Wet-work

Wet-work is one of the major causes of work-related irritant contact dermatitis. Wet-work means having hands repeatedly wet or wet for long periods during the working day. As a general guide, it means having hands wet for more than two hours a day or washing hands more than 20 times a day.

Water penetrating the horny layer cells (sometimes assisted by other chemicals) can be retained in the cells. It causes horny layer cells to swell. When the exposure to wet-work has ceased, the excess water will diffuse out and evaporate. The 'yo-yo' effect of swelling and shrinking can damage the horny layer, which in turn can affect the barrier function of the skin. It should be noted that some glove wearers may suffer irritant contact dermatitis caused by sweat trapped between the surface of the skin and the glove. The potential for this effect can be minimised in various ways and these are explained in Chapter 11.

## Natural Products

Hundreds of natural products used at work can cause irritant and allergic contact dermatitis. These products can be found in many forms including flowers, plants, spices, colouring, perfumes and animal products. In general, natural products do not present problems for the majority of workers. However, a small minority may be at risk of allergic and irritant contact dermatitis. Pre-employment assessment, monitoring for outbreaks of dermatitis and regular skin inspection will help to identify susceptible individuals. Natural rubber proteins, found in single-use latex gloves, are well-known sensitisers and have affected hundreds of people at work. Therefore, the use of single-use latex gloves should always be justified by balancing this risk against its protection and performance (Regulation 7 of the Control of Substances Hazardous to Health- COSHH) – a sensible risk management approach. Certain occupations will involve work with natural products and these can present a risk of skin disease and respiratory sensitisation. Examples are given in Table 4.1 in Chapter 4. Industry sector related information may be obtained from enforcement authorities and trade associations.

## Cosmetics and Medicines

Cosmetic products are not covered by the CHIP regulations. They are subject to cosmetic products regulations. These regulations require that the supplier of a cosmetic product must provide details of the ingredients. However, the information provided may be overwhelming to a small firm owner and this difficulty can be understood by reading the ingredients list on a shampoo bottle. On the other hand, industrial sector trade bodies are normally aware of health and safety problems, including those associated with cosmetic products. They will be able to give guidance on hazard/health risks identification and the steps necessary to control the health risks. This approach has been used effectively in many SME sectors such as hair and beauty.

## Process-Generated Substances

Several processes (e.g. welding, cutting, grinding and burning) can generate hazardous by-products (e.g. welding fume; hydrofluoric acid generated by burning PTFE in the presence of moisture). One of the ways to find out whether a process may generate by-products is either to consult a trade association or refer to process specific control guidance published by regulatory agencies. For example, HSE and NIOSH publish exposure control guidance sheets for work involving welding fume.

## Substances and Occupations

Examples of hazardous substances, and the occupations in which they may be encountered, are given in Tables 4.1 and 4.2 in Chapter 4. The information provided in these Tables should not be viewed as comprehensive for the reasons explained in Chapter 4.

## Prevalence and Incidence of Dermatitis

In some workplaces, people may be suffering from work-related skin diseases (mainly contact dermatitis) and continue to work. This means there is a prevalence of dermatitis at the workplace. This prevalence may be associated with a particular task, occupation, chemical or wet-work. For example, prevalence of irritant and allergic contact dermatitis is common in sectors such as construction, hairdressing, beauty, food manufacturing/processing, catering, cleaning and health care.

Monitoring for prevalence of dermatitis, outbreaks of dermatitis (incidence) and/or other indicators of skin disease (e.g. records of skin inspection, skin condition monitoring) is useful for hazard/risk identification. There are occasions where a new case or cases of dermatitis may appear suddenly. The causes of this outbreak may be due to various factors such as an introduction of a new chemical or a work procedure; a susceptible newcomer or an existing member of staff who has been exposed to the hazardous agent over a long period and whose skin can no longer maintain its self-repairing capability. A situation of this kind may be illustrated by the example in the box below.

> There had been an outbreak of contact dermatitis in a meat-processing factory. The investigation revealed that the major cause was the introduction of a new requirement for 30 to 40 hand washings each day. This was considered to be necessary to maintain food hygiene standards. A re-evaluation of the requirement allowed a reduced number of hand washings and a better management of food hygiene. The new procedure helped to prevent dermatitis caused by wet-work and it did not affect food hygiene standards.

## Pre-Existing Skin Diseases

Existing skin conditions can be made worse by occupational exposure to chemicals and wet-work. A pre-employment questionnaire or medical assessment may help to identify pre-existing skin conditions. The information obtained will help to initiate necessary steps for risk management. Pre-existing conditions that are relevant in occupational settings include:

- Dry skin - Some individuals may have dry skin. This condition can be seen as skin without shine and adequate hydration. In some cases, the skin may show signs of minor peeling. Skin hydration level monitoring is a useful tool for the identification of the potential for dermatitis. The monitoring is easy to carry out and is explained in Chapter 13;

- Atopic eczema - The symptoms include inflammation of the skin, which tends to flare-up from time to time. It usually starts in early childhood. People with atopic eczema may be susceptible to respiratory symptoms as well (e.g. runny nose);

- Psoriasis - People with this condition can suffer from further skin problems when exposed to chemical, biological and physical agents;

- Hypersensitive skin - Some individuals can experience symptoms of stinging, itching and burning when exposed to chemicals, warm water, and certain types of clothing, especially animal based;

- Fair skin - People with fair skin are more susceptible to attacks by UV radiation;

- Blood flow problems to the skin - People with this type of condition may have impaired barrier function of the skin and may exhibit signs similar to contact dermatitis.

## Website Information

Regulators, trade associations, trades unions and professional organisations host their own websites. These websites provide useful information on dermal exposure hazards and their control. Examples of useful websites are listed in the further reading section. Search terms such as skin disease, dermatitis, contact dermatitis, irritant contact dermatitis, allergic contact dermatitis, skin absorption, occupation and industry sector names are useful. These terms can be used in various combinations to obtain the necessary information.

## CONCLUSION

Hazard identification is an important part of DERM and this Chapter describes a number of hazard identification methods. For a vast majority of substances and products, SDSs should provide most of the answers. Nevertheless, you are encouraged to confirm with the supplier that the information provided in the SDS is accurate and adequate for your circumstances. This is important because it is well known that many SDSs fail to provide adequate information. Other sources of information will include trade associations and data given in Tables 4.1 and 4.2.

Wet-work should be considered as one of the major sources for irritant contact dermatitis. The problem can be exacerbated by other hazardous substances used in wet-work situations.

The nature of any hazardous substances generated (process-generated) during a process should be known through experience. If this is not the case, employers should seek this information from their trade associations or from control guidance sheets published by regulatory agencies.

The approaches described in this Chapter should help towards hazard identification for dermal exposure risks. However, some may argue that SMEs may find it difficult to cope with a vast array of information. Where there are difficulties, they should be able to access specialist help from their trade associations. Alternatively, information may be obtained from enforcement agencies or their websites. Several enforcement agencies have developed simple approaches to help SMEs. One such example is HSE's COSHH Essentials, which is available, free, on the internet. Among other things, COSHH Essentials provides task/sector specific control guidance sheets.

## TEST YOUR KNOWLEDGE

1. List examples of hazard identification methods. Select three examples from the list you have made and explain what help is being provided by these methods.

2. List the R-phrase numbers that will indicate the potential for effects on the skin.

3. Describe what methods manufacturers may use to provide health and safety information on hazardous substances and preparations.

4. Explain what do you understand by the terms 'wet-work' and "process-generated substances".

## FURTHER READING

**2007 TLVs and BEIs. American Conference of Governmental Industrial Hygienists (ACGIH)**, Cincinnati, USA. ISBN: 978 8824 17 69 8.

**Approved classification and labelling guide (fifth edition) L131**, HSE Books, Sudbury, UK. ISBN 0 7176 2369 6.

**CHIP for everyone, HSG228**, HSE Books, Sudbury, UK. ISBN 0 7176 2370 X.

**Control of Substances Hazardous to Health (Fifth edition)**, HSE Books, Sudbury, UK. ISBN 0 71762981 3.

**EH40/2005 Workplace exposure limits**. HSE Books, Sudbury, UK. ISBN 0 7176 2977 5.

**Pocket Guide to Chemical Hazards (2005).** National Institute for Occupational Safety and Health (NIOSH), Cincinnati, USA.

**Know your skin type.** British Skin Foundation. http://www.britishskinfoundation.org.uk

**The compilation of safety data sheets.** Approved Code of Practice (third edition) L130, HSE Books, Sudbury, UK. ISBN 0 7176 2371 8.

**Skin and Occupation.** HB Van der Walle and WP Piebenga. Centre of Skin and Occupation. Arnhem, The Netherlands. Yamanouchi Europe.

**Why do I need a safety data sheet? INDG353**. Health and Safety Executive. London, UK.

**The effect of prolonged water exposure on human skin**. I Willis, MC Major. Journal of Investigative Dermatology; 60 (1973): 166-171.

## USEFUL WEB LINKS

**European Agency for Safety and Health at Work**. www.osha.eu.int

**Globally Harmonised System of Classification and Labelling of Chemicals**. http://www.unece.org/trans/danger/publi/ghs

**Health and Safety Zone.** UNISON. http://www.unison.org.uk/safety

**Occupational Dermatoses**. National Institute for Occupational Safety and Health. http://www.cdc.gov

**Safety and Health Topics: Dermal Exposure**. Occupational Safety and Health Administration, USA. http://www.osha.gov/sltc/dermalexposure/index.html

**Skin at work**. Health and Safety Executive. UK. http://www.hse.gov.uk/skin/index.htm

**Workplace Contact Dermatitis**. Workplace Safety and Insurance Board. Ontario, Canada. www.wsib.on.ca

**Skin@work**. www.occderm.asn.au/skinatwork/links.html

*Chapter 8*

# Dermal Exposure and Surface Contamination Monitoring

## INTRODUCTION

For a chemical to cause an effect on the skin or elsewhere in the body (due to skin uptake), the skin has to be exposed to a source containing the chemical. To minimise dermal exposure, it is essential to establish which pathways are contributing to the exposure. Chapter 6 provides guidance for the identification of dermal exposure pathways. This Chapter provides practical guidance for dermal exposure and surface contamination monitoring and how the information obtained might be used for day-to-day management of dermal exposure.

Dermal exposure to chemicals is a dynamic process and is associated with the interaction between different 'compartments' such as skin, air, work-surfaces, tools, personal protective equipment (PPE) and clothing layers. Chemicals reaching the skin can travel in many directions (e.g. from the skin to PPE and from there to air and then back to skin and so on). It means that the selection of suitable monitoring methods, carrying out the monitoring and interpreting the results can be challenging.

There are many methods and tools available for dermal exposure and surface contamination monitoring. The data obtained, both qualitative and quantitative, will provide essential information for the ultimate goal of prevention or minimisation of work-related ill health caused by chemicals.

## WHY CARRY OUT DERMAL EXPOSURE AND SURFACE CONTAMINATION MONITORING?

An analysis of dermal exposure pathways in Chapter 6 will show that dermal exposure and surface contamination monitoring has an important place in exposure risk management. The list below summarises the purposes of dermal exposure and surface contamination monitoring.

- To establish which dermal exposure pathways are contributing to exposure;
- To assess the extent and frequency of dermal exposure;
- To assess which areas of the body are receiving significant dermal exposure;
- To decide which dermal exposure pathways and areas of the body require attention to achieve adequate dermal exposure control;
- To assess the effectiveness of exposure control measures. These should include mechanical, behavioural and administrative controls, such as process enclosures, local exhaust ventilation (LEV), air-islands, segregation methods, PPE, training and administrative systems;
- To raise awareness among workers about the significance of dermal exposure and surface contamination for ingestion, inadvertent inhalation exposure, contamination transfer to other areas of the workplaces and homes.
- To raise awareness about the need for effective control actions;
- To encourage changes in attitudes and behaviours among employers and employees to achieve improved controls;
- To demonstrate that internal contamination of gloves and clothing can occur;
- To inform and justify dermal exposure control approaches when challenged.

Having understood the need for dermal exposure and surface contamination monitoring, it is necessary to know: (i) what methods and procedures are available for dermal exposure and surface contamination monitoring; (ii) how the data obtained should be used in dermal exposure risk management (DERM).

## DERMAL EXPOSURE MONITORING – SOME ISSUES

Research studies report that variability in levels of dermal exposure is large between individual workers (i.e. between-workers) and for individual workers (i.e. within-worker variations - meaning measurements obtained for an individual at various times). This means that dermal exposure measurements obtained for one worker may not be used with confidence to predict the exposure of another worker or for the same worker's exposure on another day.

The observations, cited above, are equally applicable to inhalation exposure monitoring. A breathing zone air sampling result will be influenced by many factors. These include: sampler location, whether the individual is right-handed or left-handed, work practices, directional release of contaminants, influence of cross draught, and collection efficiency of the sampler (see Figure 8.1). If suitable respiratory protective equipment (RPE) is used correctly for inhalation protection, it can affect the actual exposure. The Time Weighted Average (TWA) sampling result does not take account of the amount of chemical breathed-out during the exhalation cycle or the amount taken-out by RPE. Although there are many difficulties and inaccuracies with breathing zone sampling, it is widely used for making decisions about controls.

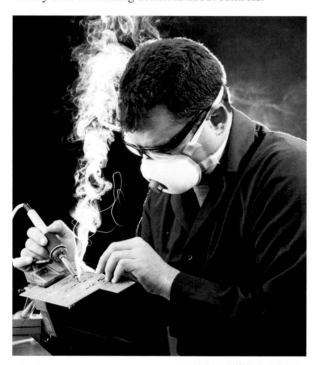

**Figure 8.1** Factors such as cross draught, plume movement, work practices, can affect the extent of exposure and exposure variability from one day to another. The plume generation and its movement was observed with the help of a Tyndall lamp. Exposure to soldering fume may lead to skin and respiratory sensitisation.

The predicament for dermal exposure monitoring is similar. However, 100% accurate and precise monitoring results are not necessary for making effective risk control decisions and their management. Therefore, there is no need to get distracted by the shortcomings of the current dermal exposure and surface contamination monitoring methods.

A number of quantitative dermal exposure and surface contamination monitoring methods are available.

However, there is no international consensus on measurement units, how the measured exposures should be interpreted for "on the skin effects" and dermal uptake. Scientists are working on these issues. In the meantime, dermal exposure and surface contamination monitoring data can be used in semi-quantitative ways to determine the extent of dermal exposure; to asses which dermal exposure pathways are contributing to total exposure; to bring about behaviour changes among employers and employees and to establish the effectiveness of exposure control systems. The next section introduces dermal exposure and surface contamination monitoring methods. The publications listed in the 'further reading' section provide detailed information.

## CONTAMINATION MONITORING METHODS

Dermal exposure and surface contamination monitoring methods may be placed into three major categories. These are:

- Interception methods,
- Removal methods, and
- Visualisation techniques.

### Interception Methods

These methods may also be referred to as "surrogate skin" techniques as they aim to inform about the extent of skin exposure. These methods use patches or pads, gloves and/or overalls for sample collection. These are worn on the skin or in close proximity to the skin. Therefore, these samplers may be considered analogous to a breathing zone sampler, which should be placed as close as is practicable to the nose and mouth.

When worn, chemicals get trapped in the sample collection medium. A suitable absorbent material performs the trapping. Chemicals recovered from the samplers are subjected to a suitable analytical procedure. Interception methods relying on *absorption* are limited to solids and low volatility liquids. Alternatively, activated charcoal cloth may be added to the collection medium as illustrated in Figure 8.2. This setup will enable volatile solvents to be sampled. In this case, the trapping action is called *adsorption*.

Homemade patches of varying sizes ($10cm^2$ to $100cm^2$) may be constructed from cotton gauze, polyester-cotton cloth, absorbent paper and polyurethane foam. In order to avoid losses to the skin or clothing, the patches should be mounted on an impervious material such as aluminium or plastic foil. However, commercially produced patch samplers are available (Figure 8.3). Patch samplers are worn at various representative locations on the body and a typical set up is shown in Figure 8.4. The locations selected will depend on the sampling protocol used.

A
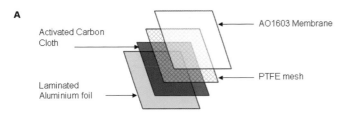

B
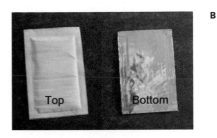

**Figure 8.2**

An example of a skin personal sampler to mimic uptake through the skin. It is achieved with the help of a membrane (e.g. A01603) selected to mimic the skin uptake rate for a given solvent vapour. This sampler is a recent innovation and could be designed for sampling aerosols and vapours. *Photograph: Courtesy of the Institute of Occupational Medicine (IOM), Edinburgh, Scotland, UK.*

**Figure 8.3** A commercial patch sampler made of surgical-grade polyurethane foam (PUF). These specially-cleaned squares can be placed in aluminium holders (left), or used on their own, for attachment to skin or clothing. *Photograph: Courtesy of SKC Ltd., Blandford Forum, Dorset, England, UK.*

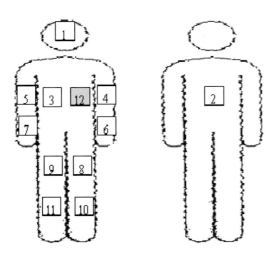

**Figure 8.4** Typical locations for patch samplers. Picture on the left shows positions in the front of the body and the picture on the right shows a position at the back. Locations chosen will be influenced by the sampling protocol.

For hand sampling, cotton gloves, (see Figure 8.5), may be used in place of a patch. For whole-body monitoring, a coverall (e.g. cotton coverall) may be used. If there is a need to monitor the head, a coverall with a hood or a hat is used. Chemicals trapped on the whole area of the glove, hat or coverall may be recovered by solvent extraction or representative patches cut from the sampler may be analysed. One of the disadvantages of glove and coverall samplers is that they can 'over' sample due to their absorption characteristics.

When an interception sampler is worn close to the skin (skin sampling zone), the sampler measures the amount

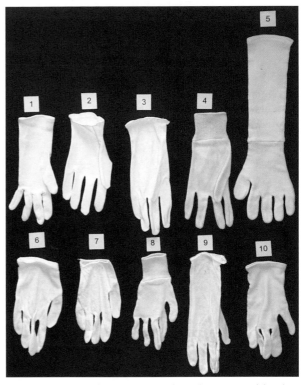

**Figure 8.5:** A range of cotton glove hand samplers. In general, hands are the most contaminated parts of the body. It is necessary to choose the right material to ensure effective collection of the contaminant; make it easy to extract the contaminant and reduce background interference (from glove material residues) during analysis.

of chemical depositing on the skin. However, as with any workplace monitoring method (e.g. breathing zone sampling, noise and vibration exposure monitoring), there is a potential for under- or over-estimation of the likely exposure. The result can be greatly influenced by the position and the sampling material used in the sampler. In addition, the uptake of a chemical through the skin is influenced by concentration gradient (as explained in Chapter 3). Therefore the amount (or mass) depositing on the skin will not provide useful information for uptake rate calculations. To do this, the amount deposited should be converted to concentration, which involves complex calculations. However, for practical purposes the amount deposited on the skin can be compared against the levels for "total daily dermal contamination giving cause for concern" and the levels are given in Table 8.2.

The need to use sampling data correctly may be explained by the following example. A study found that sheep-

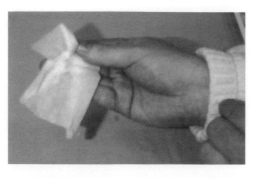

**Figure 8.6**

Wet wipe samplers. Samplers like these can be used for taking wipe samples from the skin or surfaces such as work benches, hand tools or the outsides of ventilation hoods and ducting. It is good practice to take samples from predetermined, marked up areas. This approach will facilitate comparison between samples. An example of a template is shown in Fig. 8.7.

**A** shows a general purpose wipe sampler. Contaminants in it will be analysed in a laboratory.
**B** shows a self-indicating colorimetric sampler formulated to be specific to a particular contaminant or group of compounds (e.g. aromatic amines).

*Photograph B: Courtesy of Color Laboratories Inc (CLI), Des Plaines, Illinois, USA.*

dipping workers soaked with the working solution (diluted to application concentration) of the sheep dip produced lower levels of the metabolite in urine when compared to those workers handling the concentrated sheep dip. The data obtained for both groups, however, is extremely useful for behavioural change management, assessing the extent of exposure, determining exposure pathways, demonstrating dermal absorption and explaining exposure reduction or enhancement by clothing and coveralls. The combined biological monitoring and skin sampling results will help to convey the message that workers should take greater care when handling concentrates, even though used in small volumes when compared to the working strength solutions.

Interception dermal sampling method may be used for:

- Identifying the areas of the body coming into contact with chemicals;

- Identifying which parts of the body areas are receiving significant contamination and whether they will require priority attention;

- Assessing internal contamination of gloves;

- Assessing permeation through gloves (see Chapter 11);

- Assessing the extent of protection provided by a coverall;

- Training and instruction to promote behaviour modifications.

## Removal Methods

When using removal methods, chemicals present on the skin or surfaces are removed by wiping, washing (rinsing), tape-stripping or suction and subjected to suitable analytical procedures. These methods measure only what can be removed from the skin or surfaces at the time of sampling.

Removal techniques are particularly suitable for

substances that can remain on the skin or surfaces for a relatively long time. It means the technique is suitable for dusts and sticky/low volatile substances that are poorly absorbed into the body or surfaces. It is a useful technique for substances exerting "on the skin" effects. Personal skin sampling should take place before the person has taken a break for normal hand washing and great care should be taken to ensure that the methods used do not increase the risk to the worker by damaging the skin barrier or enhancing the penetration of the substance. Surface samples should be collected before any cleaning has taken place.

## Wiping

Wiping may be carried out dry or with absorbent material soaked in water, alcohol or any other appropriate solvent (carefully selected to prevent skin damage or enhanced penetration of the substance). A variety of wipes has been employed. These include materials such as cotton balls, cotton pads, filter papers and wet-wipes. A wet wipe sampler is shown in Figures 8.6. Wipe methods are useful for sampling the skin, particularly hands, work surfaces and work tools. A template, as shown in Figure 8.7, is useful to ensure that only a pre-determined skin area or surface is wiped. This is useful for comparisons to be made between samples taken at different times. No

**Figure 8.7** An example template for marking up areas of known size for wipe or swap sampling. This approach is important for making comparisons between samples, locations and work practices.
*Photograph: Courtesy of SKC Ltd., Blandford Forum, Dorset, England, UK.*

**Figure 8.8** Typical hand washing procedure. The hand is placed in a sealable bag containing a known volume of an extracting solvent such as water or alcohol/water mixture. Vigorous shaking (for a predetermined time) is needed to dislodge the contaminant from the skin into the extracting solvent. The resulting mix can be subjected to a suitable analytical procedure.

**Figure 8.9** Tape stripping. This procedure removes a thin portion of the horny layer and the contaminants on it. This is a useful technique for surface sampling (e.g. workbenches, tools, ventilation hoods, personal protective equipment (PPE), containers and mugs).

standardised protocol exists describing the number of wipes or the amount of force that should be applied when collecting wipe samples.

## Washing

Washing methods are often applied to hands. To obtain the sample, the hand is placed in a sealable bag containing a known volume of water or other solvent (carefully selected to prevent skin damage or enhanced penetration of the substance) and vigorous shaking for a defined period is used to remove the chemical from the surface of the skin. Figure 8.8 demonstrates the principle. There is a standardised washing procedure for this method.

## Tape Stripping

Tape stripping removes a portion of the outer surface of the horny layer with the aim of quantifying chemicals present on the skin surface (see Figure 8.9). This method

**Figure 8.10a** Suction sampling. A photo-ionisation detector may be used for qualitative suction sampling of 'sticky' organic substances (e.g. phenols and amines) on surfaces (e.g. workbenches, tools and clothing).
*Photograph: Courtesy of Shawcity Ltd, Faringdon, Oxfordshire, England, UK.*

has been used extensively for the assessment of exposure to a range of chemicals such as acrylates, components of jet fuels, epoxy compounds, cadmium, arsenic, lead, and components of anti-fouling paints. It is more invasive than the interception methods and other removal techniques. As it involves the removal of a sample of the skin, this technique should be treated as biological monitoring. The procedures to be followed in the case of biological monitoring are explained later in this Chapter. This technique is also useful for sampling surfaces, such as ventilation hoods, ventilation trunks, workbenches and work tools.

## Suction

Suction sampling is used mainly to determine particulate contamination levels on surfaces. This approach was developed originally for monitoring radioactive contamination on surfaces. Compared with wipe sampling, suction sampling has a number of limitations. The sampling system needed for this technique is costly, bulky and can introduce significant sampling errors. The sample is drawn to the sampling medium with the help of vacuum action. However, in a simplest form, a personal air-sampling pump attached to a filter may be used for collecting dust contaminants from surfaces. Portable organic vapour monitors (e.g. photo-ionisation detectors) and mercury vapour samplers are useful for surface contamination monitoring (see Figure 8.10 a). Recently, a miniature vacuum sampler, as shown in Figure 8.10b,

**Figure 8.10b:** An example of a miniature vacuum skin sampler. This sampler has the potential for further development and adaptation as a time weighted average personal skin sampler for aerosols.
*Photograph: Courtesy of the Karolinska Institutet, Stockholm, Sweden.*

was tested for quantitative determination of dusts on the skin. This apparatus appears to be a tool of the future for personal suction sampling and could be adopted for TWA sampling on the skin.

## Visualisation Techniques

### Fluorescent chemicals

A fluorescent chemical deposited or retained on the skin or other surfaces is measured under ultraviolet light by appropriate detection or imaging systems. Fluorescence may be generated by the hazardous substance itself, for example polycyclic aromatic hydrocarbons, or by a tracer added to the process. Fluorescent tracer substances used include Uvitex, Tinopal and Calcoflur. The tracer used will be diluted to about 0.001% and mixed with other chemicals used in the process under investigation. Figure 8.11 shows a portable system for the detection of the tracer, whilst Figure 8.12 shows a whole body fluorescent monitor and its application, respectively.

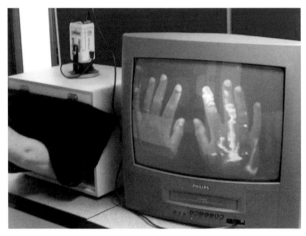

**Figure 8.11** A portable system for observing the presence of a fluorescent tracer on surfaces and skin.

The box on the left contains a UV lamp and a camera, the latter is connected to the TV screen on the right. A system like this is often used for demonstrating correct donning and doffing of gloves and application of moisturisers.

The picture on the screen shows a comparison between two hands. One on the left without any fluorescence (reference) and the hand on the right had an application of a moisturiser dosed with a fluorescent tracer. This hand shows areas that are not fluorescing indicating inadequate coverage by the moisturiser.

Fluorescent techniques lend themselves to both qualitative and quantitative exposure monitoring. They are useful for training purposes and this aspect is discussed in Chapter 12. The application of fluorescent techniques is limited by the fact that a foreign substance (a fluorescent material) has to be introduced into the process. Practical difficulties also exist, in terms of expense and the time to carry out quantitative measurement. Binding of some fluorescent tracers to the skin and surfaces may prevent the same worker or surface being measured on consecutive days.

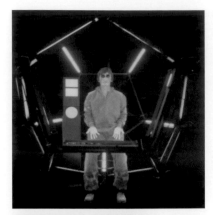

**Figure 8.12**

**A** – is showing a whole body monitoring facility for identifying fluorescent tracers.

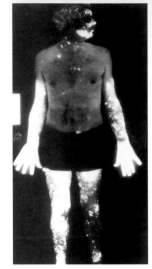

**B** – is showing contaminated parts of the body.

This extensive contamination took place during brush application of a protective coating to garden fencing panels. The coating was dosed with a fluorescent tracer to monitor skin exposure and surface contamination.

The person wore a T-shirt, light-weight shorts and a pair of sun glasses, as it was a Summer's day. Considerable exposure was caused by contaminated clothing.

Pesticides cause skin disease as well as systemic disease when absorbed through the skin.

## Tyndall Lamp

The Tyndall lamp (dust lamp) technique relies on light scattering by airborne particles and is often used for assessing or demonstrating the effectiveness of local exhaust ventilation systems. It provides an in-situ visual demonstration of dust and fumes, invisible under normal lighting, escaping from various sources. The method of operation is illustrated in Figure 8.13. A bright beam of light is shone on to the subject or an area where particles may be present or released. The observer positions himself at an angle, as shown in Figure 8.13, (in order to shield the observer's eyes from the bright light source), enabling the eyes to see the dust cloud emanating from the dust source.

This technique is a useful qualitative tool for the demonstration of dermal exposure to dusts. Dust released from the skin, coveralls, gloves and surfaces can be visualised with the help of the lamp. For example, Figure 2.5 was obtained with the help of this technique. This type of demonstration can act as a powerful training tool or for changing worker behaviour.

## Biological Monitoring

Biological monitoring (BM) is the measurement of hazardous chemicals or their metabolites in tissues, secretions, excreta or expired air, or any combination of

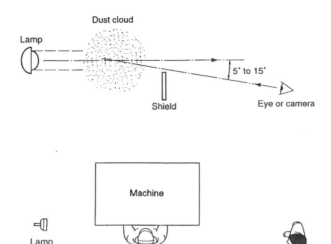

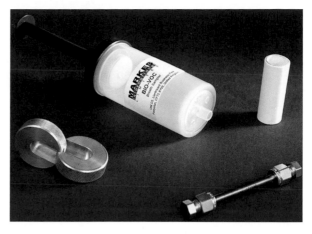

**Figure 8.14** An example breath sampler for volatile organic chemicals. A measured volume of breath can be collected in the sampling syringe. From there, it can be transferred to a thermal desorption tube (bottom) for quantification in a laboratory. The plunger helps transfer of the breath sample from the syringe to a thermal desorption tube.
*Photograph: Courtesy of Marks International Ltd., Llantrisant, Rhondda Cynon Taff, Wales, UK.*

**Figure 8.13** Typical operating method of the Tyndall lamp to observe the presence of airborne particulates. The powerful light source makes fine airborne particles visible. This technique is useful to show fine particulate contamination release from work-pieces, hands and coveralls (see Fig. 2.5) or contaminants settling on the skin or coveralls (see Fig. 6.7).

**Figure 8.15** A urine sampling pot. Samples can be sent safely by post, for analysis, providing suitable protocols are followed.

This sampling technique, where applicable, provides a cost effective approach for assessing the extent of exposure by all routes and effectiveness of control measures over a period.

these in exposed workers. Measurements reflect the total exposure levels by dermal, ingestion and inhalation routes. It means BM cannot identify the contribution by individual routes. In the context of dermal exposure, BM offers a simple way to assess whether or not there is a problem. BM is particularly useful:

- For substances that are absorbed through the skin (e.g. those carrying 'Sk' notation and a collection of R-phrases identified in Chapter 7);

- Where control of dermal exposure relies on correct selection and use of PPE;

- Where toxicity to other parts of the body is related to long-term tissue accumulation of a chemical and the toxicity cannot be related to airborne measurement taken at a particular time (e.g. cancer caused by PCBs);

- When there is an established relationship between BM data and the potential for effects elsewhere in the body. In such cases, it is one of the suitable tools for assessing the effectiveness of control measures.

Historically, medically qualified doctors and nurses carried out BM. Today, other health and safety professionals and frontline managers are able to use BM because of the development of non-invasive sampling methods (such as expired air and urine samplers). Examples of breath and urine-sampling systems are shown in Figures 8.14 and 8.15, respectively. Samples provided by the workers are subjected to analysis and the results made available to the occupational health and safety professionals and the individual who provided the sample. The data can be used to target investigations of failure of control systems.

In the GB, BM does not have legally binding exposure limits, except for lead. Under the Control of Lead at Work Regulations anyone working with lead should have blood samples analysed for lead at least once a year. For other chemicals, BM is optional but often a sensible and practical approach where Biological Monitoring Guidance Values (BMGVs) are available. Any BM results exceeding a given BMGV should trigger an investigation of the adequacy of exposure control measures.

Recently, the number of chemicals monitored in workers' by analysis of blood, urine or breath has increased significantly. BMGVs have been assigned to over 80 chemicals (16 in the GB) and are listed in EH40, American Conference of Governmental Industrial Hygienists Association - Threshold Limit Values (ACGIHA-TLV) booklet and the German toxic substances regulations guidance sheet - TRGS 903. Over 85% of these values are for a wide range of organic compounds and the rest include heavy metals such as arsenic, cadmium, mercury, nickel, cobalt and chromium.

The Health and Safety Executive (HSE) has published guidance documents for workers and employers on BM and on how to set up a BM programme. Essentially, this involves explaining to the workers why BM is being done (to check personal exposure and effectiveness of controls), what will be analysed (only the things agreed in advance and certainly not for alcohol or drugs of any kind), who will see the results and what will be done with the results (taking action to improve controls if required). It is necessary to obtain a signature denoting the workers' informed consent for the biological monitoring. An example consent form can be found in the HSE publication HSG167.

## FINDINGS OF DERMAL EXPOSURE MONITORING

Many studies assessed the relationship between work scenarios and dermal exposure patterns and found that:

- Hands were the most contaminated parts of the body for different types of work. It means significant exposure reduction is possible by making sure that bare hands are not exposed to chemicals and wet-work.

- Right hands of right-handed people were heavily exposed in comparison to left hands.

- The degree of contamination of the hands and other parts of the body varied according to the task undertaken, work practices and the prevailing conditions such as dustiness, liquid aerosol size distribution, air movement and position of the task in relation to the body and hands.

- Often, the inside of gloves was contaminated. There are many reasons for this and these are explained in Chapter 11. Contaminated gloves provide a reservoir of chemicals for dermal exposure.

- The extent of dermal exposure is generally greater for liquid-based contaminants than solids.

- During spray painting, grinding and sanding (below head level) the lower legs received significant amount of contamination. This information tells us that there is a need for adequate protection of the skin areas on legs and feet. Contaminated footwear should be handled with care to avoid cross- contamination of other parts of the body, especially hands.

- Surface contamination (work pieces, work tools, work benches, clothing and paper work) is an important route for ingestion, dermal and inadvertent inhalation exposures.

## PRACTICAL APPROACHES TO MONITORING

A prerequisite for a monitoring exercise is careful observation of the ways in which work is undertaken and identifying the likely causes of dermal exposure. Examples of simple approaches are illustrated in this section.

### Immersion

Hands may be immersed in chemicals to accomplish a task. Examples are illustrated in Figure 8.16, also in Figures 6.3. It is not necessary to carry out dermal exposure monitoring where immersion is involved. The effort should be directed to finding alternative control approaches, which will negate the need for immersion and establish adequate safe working distance (SWD) between the hands and the chemicals. Furthermore, law requires that exposure to hazardous chemicals must be prevented. Only when this is not reasonably practicable, the steps needed for adequate control of exposure should be sought.

**Figure 8.16**

The operator is immersing his gloved hand in a solvent mix to clean the insides of a paint pot.

The cuff of the glove is badly contaminated. It suggests that the work practices may allow solvents to enter between the hand and the glove via the edges of the glove. Although a degree of barrier is provided by the glove, a number of simple approaches could be applied to prevent the need for immersion and to establish adequate safe working distance (SWD). Contamination of the cuffs will present difficulties for correct removal and reuse of this reusable glove.

## Colour-Indicating Wipe and Pad Samplers

Commercially available colour-indicating wipe and pad samplers are useful for monitoring contamination on hands and surfaces. These samplers detect specific chemicals or a group of chemicals and provide rapid visual indication. Table 8.1 lists chemicals for which colour-indicator samplers are available. Colour-indicating wipe and pad samplers may be used for:

- Assessing the effectiveness of local exhaust ventilation (LEV) systems. This can be done by sampling various surfaces of the LEV system and the areas immediately outside the LEV system. The extent of contamination will provide an indication of the effectiveness of the LEV and/or work practices.

- Demonstrating good and bad work practices. Variations of skin contamination levels among a group of workers can be used for demonstrating good working methods.

- Classifying work areas for cleanliness.

- Assessing the effectiveness of cleaning and decontamination regimes.

- Demonstrating contamination transfer routes to other areas of the workplace (e.g. contaminated work-order sheets moving from process areas to offices and quality control labs; contamination of office areas through leaks in ventilation ducting).

- Assessing permeation via gloves and coveralls.

## Quantitative Dermal Exposure Monitoring of Hands

It has been established, that in general, hands receive more contamination compared to other parts of the body. Thus, as a general rule, dermal exposure monitoring of the hands should provide broad information on the efficacy of dermal exposure control measures. In order to make an exposure assessment or for assessing the efficacy of control measures, dermal exposure monitoring results for the hands may be compared against the levels given in Table 8.2. It is recommended that the sampler should be placed close to the skin surface and it should be selected to provide a representative measure of the hand contamination. Where other areas of the skin (not clothing) receive significant amount of contamination, these areas should also be assessed.

The contamination levels given in Table 8.2 are based on a proposal by the HSE. It is based on: grouping of chemicals into health hazard groups (HHGs – see Chapter 9); an amount of substance deposited on the skin during an 8-hour period that ideally should not be exceeded to minimise damage caused by skin absorption of chemicals or to the skin itself. A correction factor has been applied to HHGs A and B to take account of effects on the skin.

**Table 8.1** Sampling with colour-indicating wipes

| Chemical group | Chemical name | |
|---|---|---|
| Aromatic amines | Methylene dianiline, toluene dianiline | A |
| | Methylene bis (2-chloroaniline) (MbCOA), aniline, O-toluidine | |
| Aromatic isocyanates | Methylenebisphenyl diiosocyanate (MDI), toluene diisocyanate (TDI), | B |
| Aliphatic isocyanates | Hexamethylene diisocyanate (HDI), isophorone diisocyanate (IPDI) | |
| Metals | Cadmium, chromates, lead, mercury, nickel | |
| Acids and alkali | pH indicator | |
| Organic solvents  (a selection) | Acetone | |

**Note:** Figure A shows colour changes caused by aromatic amines. Pad in figure B shows colour change due to acetone. This pad may used for detecting specified organic solvents. These colour indicating pads are simple to use and can be used underneath gloves to assess permeation break through, glove degradation, internal contamination of gloves and surface contamination. These are useful for training, instruction and to bring about behavioural changes. *Photographs: Courtesy of Color Laboratories Inc. (CLI), Des Plaines, Illinois, USA.*

**Table 8.2** Health hazard groups and total daily dermal contamination giving cause for concern

| Health Hazard Group (HHG) | Total daily dermal contamination giving cause for concern [A,B,C] | |
|---|---|---|
| | Solids | Liquids |
| A | 5000 mg | 50 mg |
| B | 5000 mg | 50 mg |
| C | 500 mg | 10 mg |
| D | 50 mg | 1 mg |
| E | Any amount | Any amount |

**Note**

**A** - except for substances and products marked as R34 and R35 (HHG C) and used without dilution. These substances cause burns and no amount of dermal exposure should be tolerated. **B** - Substances and products with R43 classification should be treated as Group E substances.
**C** - This Table is based on Developing COSHH Essentials: Dermal Exposure, Personal Protective Equipment and First Aid. ANI Garrod and R Rajan-Sithamparanadarajah. Annals of Occupational Hygiene; 47 (2003): 577-588. and Calculation of maximum dermal doses that should not be exceeded based on systemic toxicity criteria. P Ridgway and Rajan-Sithamparanadarajah. To be published.

## EXAMPLES OF CASE STUDIES

### (i) Assessing Dermal Exposure Pathways

Methylene bis (2-chloroaniline) (MbOCA) is used in the production of polyurethane elastomers. It is a solid at room temperature, but easily absorbed via unbroken skin and can cause bladder cancer. Although LEV systems are used for controlling the release of MbOCA dust and vapour, most exposure is via the skin and surface contamination due to poor handling techniques and spills of molten MbOCA and mixtures containing MbOCA. Because MbOCA is used at around 100°C gloves are often chosen for their insulating properties rather than chemical protection. During use, gloves can be easily contaminated and the contaminated gloves and surfaces can contribute to dermal exposure as well as inadvertent inhalation exposure.

Biological monitoring (BM) and skin/surface sampling was used for assessing the efficacy of controls. Surface sampling found MbOCA contamination on LEV hoods (Figure 8.17), inside gloves, on work surfaces, tools, clothing and hands. The sampling also provided information on contamination transport, by hands, cloths and papers used for progress monitoring, to other parts of the work areas (rest rooms, teacups and offices). BM was applied to assess long term effectiveness of controls.

In another situation, workers handling sealed MbOCA containers showed signs of exposure to MbOCA (assessed by BM). Further investigation, by surface sampling, showed that the outsides of the containers had a fine film of MbOCA. It was established that this contamination occurred at the point of production and packaging.

In both cases, it was clear that behaviour modifications were necessary to minimise the exposure to MbOCA. To

**Figure 8.17** This figure shows dust (fine yellowish) contamination on the ventilation hood (outside) with a very toxic substance methylene bis 2-chloroaniline (MbCOA). This contamination could have been caused by inadequate design or incorrect operation or use of the local exhaust ventilation system (LEV). Surface sampling was used to assess the extent of the contamination.

achieve this, a graded contamination colour chart, based on MbOCA concentration (using known concentrations), was created and an example is shown in Figure 8.18. Routine wipe sampling was used to assess the extent of contamination by comparison against the colour chart. Biological monitoring (urine samples) helped to establish the extent of exposure by all routes. These approaches were used to demonstrate the need for good work practices and improved control methods. The end result was a significant reduction in exposure to MbOCA and this was achieved in part by significant behaviour modifications by employers and employees.

### (ii) Dermal Absorption of Vapours

Biological monitoring is useful for demonstrating that liquids and solvent vapours can easily be absorbed through the skin and this absorption can contribute to the body burden. It has been shown that for glycol ethers (used widely in paints and printing inks) dermal

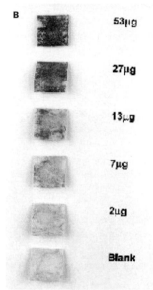

53μg

27μg

13μg

7μg

2μg

Blank

**Figure 8.18**

**A** is showing the colour intensity of a sampling pad indicating the extent of surface of contamination (approximately 50μg).

**B** is showing a home-made calibration chart for semi quantitative monitoring of methylene bis 2-chloroaniline (MbCOA) contamination on surfaces and hands.

absorption of vapours at or near the inhalation exposure limits can account for 10 to 75% of total daily body burden. This means that just wearing respiratory protective equipment is not good enough for effective protection. Controls should be in place for a significant reduction in airborne concentrations and for controlling dermal exposure to the solvents. This case study shows that employers should pay greater attention to dermal exposure of liquids and vapours, especially to those substances with skin notation.

### (iii) Inhalation of Dusts Resulting from Dermal Exposure

Inhalation exposure to silica dust can lead to serious respiratory diseases. For this reason, construction and quarry workers tend to wear RPE. However, dusts generated during the work can settle on coveralls, hands and face, when control measures at source are inadequate. Figure 2.5 shows fine dust being liberated from the coverall. This demonstration was created with the help of the Tyndall lamp and it shows the potential for inadvertent inhalation exposure resulting from dermal/surface

exposure. If the contaminated coverall is taken home (or if the silica dust has settled on the street clothing inside the coverall), it will provide a real potential for third party (family members) exposures. If the dust was cement, exposure may lead to skin sensitisation and/or serious burns to the skin as shown in Figures 2.2 and 3.7.

### (iv) Contamination of Body Areas during Airless Spray Painting

A monitoring exercise was conducted during airless spray-painting of both inside and outside of bulk goods containers. Paint was dosed with Uvitex fluorescent dye tracer to aid dermal exposure monitoring. Contaminated coveralls and hands were analysed with the help of a UV light source. In this study, surrogate fluorescent sampling methods showed that the lower legs of the body received the highest proportion of contamination followed by upper legs and torso. The evidence shows that people should pay greater attention when removing coveralls and footwear. Paint on the coveralls or footwear can be transferred to unprotected hands and other parts of the skin. This secondary contamination on the skin may be absorbed, ingested or inhaled. If the paint contained metals such as chromium or lead, the importance of dermal exposure and the requirement for careful removal and disposal of coverall would become very relevant. Chromium is a skin irritant and a sensitiser. Lead causes health effects on other parts of the body.

### (v) Potential for Ingestion due to Dermal Exposure

A number of publications have reported that inadvertent ingestion of chemicals can take place at work. The main contributor was hand contamination. It was estimated that in the UK alone one in six workers may be involved in tasks where inadvertent ingestion exposure could contribute to their body burden. These can take place in a number of tasks and jobs involving metals, metal compound, pharmaceuticals, pesticides, insecticides, fibrous materials and organic compounds. For example, workers removing lead paints from bridges and ship decks face the potential for significant exposure via hands-to-mouth contact and food contamination. The exposure of the hands can take place due to deposition; contact with contaminated work surfaces, tools and clothing; direct handling of work pieces and waste materials. In these situations, removal techniques will provide useful information.

### (vi) Dermal Exposure Pathways and Photographs

Often photographs taken at workplaces will serve to demonstrate dermal exposure, the consequences of dermal exposure and the need for adequate control. For example, Figures 2.5, 6.1 to 6.8, 8.15, 8.16 and 8.17 show the value of photographs in risk management. Professionals should make use of photographs to improve attitudes and behaviours, but the selection and use of photographs should be representative of the context in which they are used.

The example case studies illustrate the immense value of dermal exposure/surface monitoring in risk management. The most important lesson for a practical risk manager is that dermal exposure/surface monitoring techniques should be used for defined purposes rather than just collecting exposure data.

## CONCLUSION

Dermal exposure can be a significant contributor to overall exposure to chemicals. It can lead to skin and systemic diseases. Furthermore, chemicals on the skin and surfaces can contribute to inadvertent inhalation exposure and ingestion. They can, also, contribute to third party exposures. Simple dermal exposure/surface monitoring methods will provide useful information on dermal exposure pathways and effectiveness of control systems. They are also useful for worker training, behaviour modification and forensic investigation. Readers are encouraged to use suitable dermal exposure/surface monitoring methods as an essential part of risk management.

## TEST YOUR KNOWLEDGE

1. Explain some of the important reasons for carrying out dermal exposure/surface monitoring.

2. There are three main types of dermal exposure/surface monitoring methods. What are they?

3. List four examples of surface monitoring methods and explain two of them in detail.

4. Explain how you would use the Tyndall lamp technique in dermal exposure control.

## FURTHER READING

**2007 TLVs and BEIs. American Congress of Governmental Industrial Hygiene Association (ACGIHA)**, Cincinnati, USA. ISBN: 978 8824 17 69 8

**A UK approach to help small firms control health risks from chemicals: toxicological considerations**. IM Brooke. Annals of Occupational Hygiene; 42 (1998): 377-390.

**An introduction to a UK scheme to help small firms control health risks from chemicals**. RM Russell, SC Maidment, I Brooke, MD Topping. Annals of Occupational Hygiene; 42 (1998): 367-376.

**Are variance components of exposure heterogeneous between time periods and factories in the European carbon black industry?** M Van Tongeren, I Burstyn, H Kromhout and K Gardiner. Annals of Occupational Hygiene; 50 (2006): 55-64.

**Assessment of skin exposure to nickel, chromium, and cobalt by acid wipe sampling and ICP-MS.** C Liden, S Skare, B Lind, G Nise, M Vahter. Contact Dermatitis; 54 (2006): 233-238.

**Assessment of dermal exposure during airless spray painting using a quantitative visualisation technique**. DH Brouwer, CM Lansink, JW Cherrie and J Van Hemmen. Annals of Occupational Hygiene; 44 (2000): 543-549.

**Biological Monitoring in the Workplace Information for employees on its application to chemical exposure (INDG245)**. HSE Books, Sudbury, UK. ISBN 0 7176 1450 6.

**Biological monitoring in the Workplace: A guide to its practical application to chemical exposure (HSG167)**. HSE Books, Sudbury, UK. ISBN 0 7176 1279 1.

**Biologically relevant assessment of dermal exposure**. JW Cherrie and A Robertson. Annals of Occupational Hygiene; 39 (1995): 387-392.

**Biological workplace tolerance values – BAT values,** TRGS 903. Deutsche Forschungsgemeinschaft. Germany.

**Calculation of maximum dermal doses that should not be exceeded based on systemic toxicity criteria**. P Ridgway and Rajan-Sithamparanadarajah. To be published.

**COSHH Essentials. Easy steps to control chemicals**. HSG193. HSE Books, Sudbury, UK. ISBN 0 7176 2421 8. www.cossh-essentails.org

**Dermal exposure assessment**. T Schneider, JW Cherrie, R Vermeulen and H Kromhout. Annals of Occupational Hygiene; 44 (2000): 493-499.

**Dermal exposure to dry powder spray paints using PXRF and the method of Dirichlet tessellations**. M Roff, DA Bagon, H Chambers, EM Dilworth and N Warren. Annals of Occupational Hygiene; 48 (2004): 257-266.

**Dermal exposure to chromium in the grinding of stainless and acid-proof steel**. M Makinen and M Linnainmaa. Annals of Occupational Hygiene; 48 (2004): 197-202.

**Dermal exposure to electroplating fluids and metal working fluids in the UK**. M Roff, DA Bagon, H Chambers, EM Dilworth and N Warren. Annals of Occupational Hygiene; 48 (2004): 209-218.

**Dermal exposure to styrene in the fibreglass reinforced plastics industry**. K Eriksson and L Wiklund. Annals of Occupational Hygiene; 48 (2004): 203-208.

**Dermal exposure to terpine resin acids in Swedish carpentry workshops and sawmill**. K Erikson, L Wiklund and L Larsson. Annals of Occupational Hygiene; 48 (2004): 267-276.

**Developing COSHH Essentials: Dermal Exposure, Personal Protective Equipment and First Aid**. ANI Garrod and R Rajan-Sithamparanadarajah. Annals of Occupational Hygiene; 47 (2003): 577-588.

**Development of a biologically relevant dermal sampler**. FE Lindsay, S Semple, A Robertson and JW Cherrie. Annals of Occupational Hygiene; 50 (2006): 85-94.

**Deutsche Forschungsgemeinschaft List of MAK and BAT values 2005**. Commission for the Investigation of Health Hazards of Chemical Compounds in the Work Area. Report No. 40 Wiley VCH Verlag. Germany.

**EH40/2005 Workplace exposure limits**. HSE Books, Sudbury, UK. ISBN 0 7176 2977 5.

**Factors affecting the extent of dermal absorption of solvent vapours: a human volunteer study**. K Jones, J Cocker, LJ Dodd, I Fraser. Annals of Occupational Hygiene; 47 (2003): 45-50.

**Hand wash and manual skin wipes**. DH Brouwer, MF Boeniger and, J van Hemmen. Annals of Occupational Hygiene; 44 (2000): 501-510.

**Health Hazard Evaluation Reports.** www.cdc.gov/niosh/hhe/reports/pdfs

**Human Tissues Act 2004**. HM Stationary Office, London, UK. www.opsi.gov.uk/acts/acts2004/20040030.htm

**How important is inadvertent ingestion of hazardous substances at work.** JW Cherrie, S Semple, Y Christopher, A Saleem, GW Hughson and A Phillips. Annals of Occupational Hygiene; 50 (2006): 693-704.

**Measuring dust on skin with a small vacuuming sampler – A comparison with other sampling techniqu**es. L Lundgren, L Skare and C Liden. Annals of Occupational Hygiene; 50 (2006): 95-103.

**Occupational Hygiene Assessment of sheep dipping practices and processes. IOM Report TM/93/03 (1993)**. KJM Niven, AJ Scott, S Hagen, ER Waclawki, M Lovett, B Cherrie, PL Bodsworth, A Robertson, A Elder, J Cocker, B Nutlley, and M Roff. Institute of occupational medicine, Edinburgh, Scotland, UK.

**Patterns of dermal exposure to hazardous substances in European Union workplace**s. R Rajan-Sithamparanadarajah, M Roff, P Delgado, K Eriksson, W Fransman, JHJ Gijsbers, G Hughson, M Makinen and JJ Van Hemmen. Annals of Occupational Hygiene; 48 (2004): 285-297.

**Potential dermal exposure during the painting process in car body repair shops**. P Delgado, J Porcell, I Abril, N Torres, A Teran, and A Zugasti. Annals of Occupational Hygiene; 48 (2004): 229-236.

**Potential exposure of hands inside protective gloves – a summary of data from non-agricultural pesticide surveys**. ANI Garrod, AM Phillips and JA Pemberton. Annals of Occupational Hygiene; 45 (2001): 55-60.

**Surface and Dermal Monitoring for Toxic Exposures.** SA Ness. Van Nostrand Reinhold, New York, USA. ISBN 0 442 01465 1.

**The dust lamp. Methods for the determination of hazardous substances (MDHS 82)**, HSE Books, Sudbury, UK. ISBN 0 7176 1362 3.

**Use of patches and whole body sampling for the assessment of dermal exposure**. A Soutar, S Semple, RJ Aitken and A Robertson. Annals of Occupational Hygiene; 44 (2000): 511-518.

**Use of qualitative and quantitative fluorescence techniques to assess dermal exposure**. JW Cherie, DH Brouwer, M Roff, R Vermeulen and H Kromhout. Annals of Occupational Hygiene; 44 (2000): 519-522.

**Variability of task-based dermal exposure measurements from a variety of workplaces**. H Kromhout, W Fransman, R Vermeulen, M Roff and JJ Van Hemmen. Annals of Occupational Hygiene; 48 (2004): 187-196.

**Variation of exposure between workers in homogeneous groups**. SM Rappaport. American Industrial Hygiene Association Journal; 54 (1995): 654-662.

**Workplace exposure – Strategy for the evaluation of dermal exposure. CEN-Technical Report No. CEN/TR 15278.** European Committee for Standardization, Brussels, Belgium.

# Part 4

# DERMAL EXPOSURE RISK MANAGEMENT

*Chapter 9*

# Dermal Exposure Risk Management

## INTRODUCTION

Part 1 of this book describes how dermal exposure to chemicals and *wet-work* can cause serious harm to people at work. It can, also, cause significant economic and social impact. Hand exposure accounts for the majority of cases of skin disease. Contamination of the skin and surfaces, such as clothing, gloves, work benches and tools, provides opportunities for inadvertent inhalation exposure and ingestion. Substantial health, economic and social benefits can be achieved by implementing sensible Dermal Exposure Risk Management (DERM) measures. This will include implementation of adequate safe working distance (SWD) between hands and contaminants.

A sensible DERM will:

● Involve simple risk assessments;

● Deal with risks causing significant harm;

● Use minimum paper work;

● Take account of human factors;

● Use simple practical control measures, where possible; and

● Not rely solely on personal protective equipment (PPE).

Application of these principles will help to minimise poor management practices; deal with barriers to change, such as negative attitudes and behaviours; and deliver significant reductions in ill health caused by skin exposure to chemicals and wet-work.

The aims of this Chapter are two-fold. The first aim is to introduce simple approaches to DERM. The second is to generate confidence that in the majority of cases, it is relatively easy and simple to carry out dermal exposure assessments and establish suitable dermal exposure control measures.

## RISK ASSESSMENT

The requirements to carry out suitable and sufficient risk assessment are enshrined in law. The essential elements of suitable and sufficient risk assessment are described in Chapter 5. This section provides help for carrying out suitable and sufficient dermal exposure risk assessments.

### Factors Causing Skin Exposure

The important contributory factors to skin exposure are listed below:

● Using hands as a working tool rather than as an aid. This action leads to immersion and/or direct contact.

● Work methods causing contamination of surfaces such as tools and paper work. Surfaces should be regularly cleaned. A monitoring regime should be in place to assess the extent of cleanliness or cross contamination;

● Contaminants in air depositing on the skin. Extract ventilation systems and enclosures should be designed and operated to control exposure by all routes and to prevent contamination spreading outside the hood and/or ventilation ducting;

● Splashes landing on the skin. Suitable handling systems will prevent or minimise splashing;

● Using internally contaminated gloves. Incorrect putting-on and taking-off (donning and doffing) of gloves can lead to internal contamination. Suitable training for correct donning and doffing and regular examination of gloves is essential. Contaminated protective clothing and footwear causes skin contamination, inhalation and ingestion;

● Failing to remove contamination on the skin, as soon as is practicable. Contaminants on the skin may act as a reservoir causing damage to the skin or passing through the skin to cause damage to other parts of the body.

## Components of Skin Exposure Assessment

Consider the following when carrying out exposure risk assessments for skin exposure to chemicals and wet-work:

- Physical state of the hazardous substance, product or material. It will help to establish dermal exposure pathways and design effective control measures;

- Hazardous properties of the substance, product or material;

- Health risks including 'on the skin' and effects on other parts of the body, if entry is gained;

- Dermal exposure pathways;

- Which parts of the body are exposed;

- Use pattern. This will include the level (extent), duration and frequency of exposure;

- Who is being exposed? This will include third parties outside the workplace;

- Work activities contributing to dermal exposure so that control measures can be directed to activities presenting significant exposure risks;

- Potential for occluded exposure. Chemicals and water can be trapped in clothing, inside gloves and folded areas of the skin;

- Work methods. Consider the need to use abrasive action, abrasive materials or the need to use sharp objects. These will influence the potential for direct damage to the skin and the selection and use of PPE;

- Potential for inhalation and ingestion resulting from dermal exposure and surface contamination.

Based on the consideration of the above issues, identify the steps needed for prevention or adequate control of skin exposure. Suitable steps for adequate control of exposure will include process design, material control, enclosure, tools and other methods for establishing adequate SWD; PPE; skin care products and administrative controls.

A number of other work-related factors will influence the suitability of assessments and control actions. These include:

- Working in high or low humidity environments. High humidity environments can cause excess water retention on the skin and clothing. The retained water and wet areas can act as a reservoir for chemicals. In this case, attention should be given to air movement, clothing, water salt balance and work-rest regimes. A low humidity environment can dehydrate the skin. To counteract the drying effects, skin moisturising creams should be applied.

- Wind. It can take away water from the skin and transport contaminants to and from the skin. Regular application of skin care products is necessary.

- Excessive temperature or exposure to the sun. For example construction workers may suffer from damaged skin due to excessive exposure to the sun during the Summer months. Attention should be given to the types of protective clothing selected and the need to use "sun-blocking" creams.

## EXAMPLES OF SIMPLE APPROACHES TO DERM

A simple generic approach is introduced in this book. It is known as APC, which stands for:

- ✓ Avoid contact with the skin,
- ✓ Protect the skin, and
- ✓ Check for early signs of disease.

The APC approach, developed by the Health and Safety Executive (HSE), is intended for communicating dermal exposure control messages in a simple way. This approach is designed to grab the attention of the audience. Ideally, each element of the APC approach should not contain more than 5 key control messages.

The Chapters following this will describe examples of practical control measures using the APC approach. The Chapter on "avoid contact with the skin" will describe examples of practical approaches for prevention or adequate control of dermal exposure. It will explain why it is necessary to establish adequate SWD between the source giving rise to the contaminant and the skin. The Chapter on "protect the skin" will deal with PPE, personal hygiene, welfare facilities and skin care products. The Chapter on "check for early signs of disease" will describe simple approaches for the early detection of skin diseases.

This section describes examples of simple approaches for the effective implementation of DERM.

### (A) An Industrial Sector-Based Approach

An industrial sector-based approach is a powerful tool for effective DERM and is equally applicable for managing other health and safety risks. Trade associations, professional and enforcement bodies are the key players for developing industrial sector-based approaches. This approach is becoming common in the UK, USA, Europe and Australia.

The approach is explained with the help of a campaign developed for controlling contact dermatitis in the hairdressing sector. This sector consists mainly of small enterprises. In general, they do not have in-house health and safety expertise and rely on external sources. Table 9.1 opposite summarises the approach.

**Table 9.1** DERM and dermatitis in hairdressing

| ISSUE OR PROBLEM | Dermatitis in hairdressing is a major problem. This fact is recognised by enforcement authorities, the industry and teaching establishments. |
|---|---|
| **Health Risks** | Irritant and allergic contact dermatitis. |
| **Hazardous substances processes** | Chemicals in hairdressing products; natural rubber proteins in single-use latex gloves; and wet-work. Shampooing, colouring, perming and highlighting. |
| **Activities** | Shampooing, washing, rinsing, colouring, bleaching and highlighting tasks present significant risks. Information available indicated that young trainee hairdressers are the high risk group when compared to others. |
| **Dermal exposure pathways** | Immersion, direct and surface contacts are the main routes. Hands and wrists are at risk. Others include eyes, face and neck areas. |
| **Use Pattern** | Significant level of exposure, every client, about 10 times a day, each working day. |
| **Who is at risk** | Trainees and stylists are the most at risk groups |
| **Human factors and resistance to change** | Trainees are expected to do most of the wet-work. Customers do not like gloves; gloves can snag hair; when gloves are worn one cannot feel the temperature of the water to achieve the correct mixing; job rotation should eliminate dermatitis; skin will harden up with time; single-use powdered latex gloves are cheap; "barrier creams" will protect. A high level of trainee turnover due to dermatitis. |
| **Controls** | HSE took the lead. Issues researched, user surveys carried out, control solutions developed, tested and discussed with industry, users, suppliers and enforcement authorities. Single-use, all-round smooth disposable vinyl or nitrile gloves of about 300mm in length. Training for correct donning and doffing of gloves. Implementation of hand hygiene including regular use of moisturisers. Fact-based answers to deal with resistance to change issues. |
| **Communication** | Key messages and a training module were developed in association with stakeholders. Tools for communication were developed including a website known as 'Bad Hand Day'. National seminars. Suppliers and others engaged to take the key messages and samples of skin care products. Case histories of sufferers used in communications. |
| **Outputs** | Seminars; websites; free samples of gloves and skin care creams; posters on gloves, hand hygiene and skin check; adverts; training modules; working together with stakeholders for one goal, based on agreed approaches. |
| **Outcomes** | Significant improvements in the uptake of control measures. Resistance to change minimised. Stakeholders' commitment to effect change. Individual employers need not undertake individual assessment or develop control measures. This approach leads to cost savings and level playing. Expect significant reduction in dermatitis in the medium to long term. |

Sector-based approaches should be encouraged when:

- Small firms are involved.
- Hazards and risks are well established.
- Control solutions are simple and easy to implement across the sector.
- Trade bodies have expertise and resources.
- Ill health statistics warrant a concerted action.
- Wet-work is a major concern.

## (B) Task-Based Control Guidance Sheets

Task-based control guidance sheets (CGS) are another useful way for implementing DERM. A typical source for service sector tasks is COSHH Essentials (CE). The CGSs are ready-to-use and downloadable, free, via the Internet. The recommended main options for dermal exposure control are PPE and procedures for early detection of skin disease. These sheets do not consider in detail human factor issues and SWD.

## (C) Risk Rating

Where a work activity is undertaken at a fixed production site and Risk phrases (R-phrases) for the materials used are readily available, CE provides control approaches for many tasks. At present, CE is not well geared for dermal exposure risk assessment and control. It is suggested that the rules described in this section can be applied for skin exposure control (see Table 9.5). In order to explain the rules, this section summarises the CE risk rating system.

The CE scheme allocates health hazards to one of five health hazard groups using R-phrases (a detailed explanation of R-phrases is in Chapter 7). These are shown in Table 9.2. The potential for inhalation exposure is classified on the basis of amount used and extent of dustiness or volatility. This is shown in Table 9.3.

**Table 9.2** Health Hazard Groups (HHGs)

| A Irritants | B Harmful | C Toxic | D Very Toxic | E Special |
|---|---|---|---|---|
| R36 | R20 | R23 | R26 | R42 |
| R38 | R21 | R24 | R27 | R45 |
| R66 | R22 | R25 | R28 | R46 |
| | | R37 | R40 | R49 |
| | | R41 | R48/21 | R40 |
| | | R43 | R48/22 | R68 |
| | | R34* | R60 | R39/24 |
| | | R35* | R61 | R39/27 |
| | | | R62 | R48/24 |
| | | | R63 | R48/25 |
| | | | | R68/21 |

*\* – for corrosive substances any amount of dermal exposure is unacceptable*

The generic control approach is allocated according to the health hazard group, amount used and dustiness or volatility band as shown in Table 9.4. An assessment can be carried out electronically using e-COSHH essentials (e-CE) at www.coshh-essentials.org.uk. At the end of the process, the users will be offered a control approach. The description of the control approaches are as follows: Control Approach 1- General ventilation; Control Approach 2 – Engineering control; Control Approach 3 – Containment; Control Approach 4 – Special, requiring technical advice from an occupational health professional. At the end of the assessment cycle, users will be able to download the recommended control guidance sheets for inhalation exposure control and PPE for skin hazards.

**Table 9.3** Potential inhalation exposure bands

| DUSTINESS/VOLATILITY BANDS | PHYSICAL PROPERTY |
|---|---|
| Low dustiness solid | Pellets, waxy flakes and pill-like solids that do not break up easily |
| Low volatility liquid | Vapour pressure <0.5kPa or boiling point > or =150°C, used at room temperature |
| Medium dustiness solid | Crystalline granular solids and dust. Visible and settles quickly |
| Medium volatility liquid | Vapour pressure 0.5 –25kPa or boiling point between 50°C and 150°C, used at room temperature |
| High dustiness solid | Fine powder, fine mist and fume. Dust cloud, mist or fume is formed and remains in the air for several minutes |
| High volatility | Vapour pressure >25kPa or boiling point between <50°C, used at room temperature |
| AMOUNT (QUANTITY) USED/OPERATOR | UNIT |
| Small | Grams or millilitres (a few ounces, around a cupful) |
| Medium | Kilograms or litres (1-100kg, up to 55 gallons) |
| Large | Tonnes or cubic metres (tanker or lorry loads) |

**Table 9.4** COSHH Essentials control approaches for inhalation exposure

| Amount used | Low dustiness or volatility | Medium Volatility | Medium Dustiness | High dustiness or volatility |
|---|---|---|---|---|
| Health Hazard Group A | | | | |
| Small | 1 | 1 | 1 | 1 |
| Medium | 1 | 1 | 1 | 2 |
| Large | 1 | 1 | 2 | 2 |
| Health Hazard Group B | | | | |
| Small | 1 | 1 | 1 | 1 |
| Medium | 1 | 2 | 2 | 2 |
| Large | 1 | 2 | 3 | 3 |
| Health Hazard Group C | | | | |
| Small | 1 | 2 | 1 | 2 |
| Medium | 2 | 3 | 3 | 3 |
| Large | 2 | 4 | 4 | 4 |
| Health Hazard Group D | | | | |
| Small | 2 | 3 | 2 | 3 |
| Medium | 3 | 4 | 4 | 4 |
| Large | 3 | 4 | 4 | 4 |
| Health Hazard Group E | | | | |
| For this hazard group substances, choose control approach 4 | | | | |

### Rules for Skin Exposure Control

The rules proposed in Table 9.5 will apply along with the provision of suitable personal hygiene measures including skin care products. These are described in Chapter 12. Where the substance is known to cause irritant or allergic contact dermatitis and the exposure takes place on a daily basis, regular skin checks should be undertaken by a responsible person. This aspect is detailed in Chapter 13.

### (D) Control Measures Already in Place

Where there are existing control systems and procedures, compare them against the CE approach described in C above. Establish whether the control systems in place match up with those recommended by the CE approach and the rules for skin exposure control. If there are significant differences, establish whether there are valid reasons for the variations and ensure exposure is

adequately controlled. CE recommends good practices for exposure control. Wipe sampling of surfaces, skin and clothing will provide a good indication of the control efficacy.

### (E) Work Undertaken at Temporary Locations

Where control advice is available from trade associations, these may be used. Alternatively, those published by regulatory agencies can be used.

## CONSEQUENCES OF INEFFECTIVE DERMAL EXPOSURE CONTROL

Several publications listed in Chapter 3 photographically show the effects of chemicals on the skin and explain the reasons they occurred. Examples in Table 3.1 illustrate the consequences of dermal absorption of chemicals. HSE's Rash Decisions video describes examples of personal suffering.

Several civil claims have been awarded for skin diseases caused by chemicals and wet-work. Third parties have been awarded compensation because they were able to establish that their ill health was caused by contaminants brought home from work. An example is given in Chapter 6.

Enforcement authorities are paying increasing attention to dermal exposure and the harm resulting. Hundreds of enforcement actions have been taken for inadequate control of dermal exposure to chemicals and wet-work. In the UK, these translate into enforcement authorities issuing warning letters, Prohibition Notices (PNs), Improvement Notices (INs) and initiating court proceedings. Germany takes a different approach to enforcement and it is achieved in the main with the help of workplace insurance boards. In the USA, the Occupational Safety and Health Administration (OSHA) issues violation notices and in-situ fines. The US-National Institute for Occupational Safety and Health (NIOSH) carries out investigations involving dermal exposure risks and make recommendations for control actions.

Companies have been fined thousands of pounds for non-compliance. For example, a company was fined £100,000 for causing allergic contact dermatitis to three of their employees. Furthermore, the court awarded £30,000 towards prosecution costs. The expenditure did not stop there. Other expenditures included payments to defence and prosecution lawyers, civil claims, loss of production and costs incurred by the national health hospitals, general practice surgeries and the families of the victims.

**Table 9.5** Rules for skin exposure control

| Health Hazard Group | Amount used | Control approaches |
|---|---|---|
| A, B, C | Small | CE control approach 1 or 2 as recommended. Direct hand contact, clean as soon as is practicable. <br><br> R34, R35 and R43 substances use suitable gloves. <br><br> R43 substances establish pre-existing medical conditions. If there are concerns seek medical help. |
| ABC | Medium | CE control approach 1 or 2. Hand immersion and/or direct contact, establish adequate SWD, if this not practical justify and provide suitable gloves. Implement measures to prevent or minimise contamination of clothing and surfaces. <br><br> CE control approach 3 – design and implementation of control measures at source and work practices should prevent contamination dispersal outside the extraction zone. <br><br> R34, R35 and R43 apply control approach 3. Specialist designing the control should give advice on skin exposure control. Alternatively control approach 4. |
| ABC | Large | CE control approach 1 or 2. Hand immersion and/or direct contact, consider unacceptable. Implement adequate SWD. Prevent splashing. <br><br> Control approach 1 – clean surface as often as possible and at the end of the task. <br><br> CE control approach 2 – design and implementation of control measures at source and work practices should prevent contaminant dispersal, including splashes, outside the extraction zone. <br><br> Control approach 3 – Specialist designing the control should give advice on skin exposure control. Surface and skin monitoring. Biological monitoring where available. |
| D | Small | CE control approach 2 – design and implementation of control measures at source and work practices should prevent contaminant dispersal outside the extraction zone. Ensure adequate SWD is present. Use suitable gloves. Clean surface as often as is practicable and after the task is complete. Surface and hand monitoring. Use Tyndall lamp to observe contamination release from control sources and clothing. <br><br> CE control approach 3 – Specialist designing the control should give advice on skin exposure control. Biological monitoring where available. |
| D | Medium or Large | CE control approach 3 – specialist designing the control should give advice on skin exposure control. Regular inhalation, skin and surface contamination monitoring. BM where available. Use Tyndall lamp to observe contamination release from control sources and clothing. |
| E | Any amount | Seek specialist advice |

## CONCLUSION

Readers are encouraged to use simple approaches for controlling skin exposure to chemicals and wet-work. Initiatives for controlling inhalation exposure should not be considered in isolation. They should consider other routes of exposure. DERM should take account of human factor issues, resistance to change and practical application of control measures. SWD approach should be put in place for achieving adequate control of dermal exposure. The "APC" approach is a simple method for communicating skin exposure control measures.

Employers should be aware that failures to meet the requirements for adequate control of dermal exposure to chemicals and wet-work can give rise to serious consequences including wasted money and other resources.

## TEST YOUR KNOWLEDGE

1. Select two tasks in your workplace involving hazardous chemicals and apply the risk rating approach described in C above. Compare the control recommendations against those already in place. Assess whether the existing engineering control measures are suitable for adequate control of exposure by all routes. Is there adequate SWD in place for dermal exposure control? Describe your reasons in detail.

## FURTHER READING

**A toolkit for dermal risk assessment and management: an overview.** R Oppl, F Kalberlah, PG Evans et al. Annals of Occupational Hygiene; 47 (2003): 629-640.

**Allergy Nurse's Compensation Deal.** BBC News: 26.06.2006. BBC, London, UK. http://news.bbc.co.uk/go/pr/fr/-/1/hi/england/beds/bucks/herts/5123160.stm

**Company Fined £100,000. Employees suffered from painful allergic dermatitis over four year period.** HSE News Release: E098:06: 5 10 2006. Health and Safety Executive, London, UK.

**Developing COSHH Essentials: Dermal exposure, personal protective equipment and first aid.** ANI Garrod and R Rajan-Sithamparanadarajah. Annals of Occupational Hygiene; 47 (2003): 577-588.

**DREAM: A method for semi-quantitative dermal exposure assessment.** B van-Wendel-DE-Joode, DH Brouwer, R Vermeulen, JJ van Hemmen, D Heederik, H Kromhout. Annals of Occupational Hygiene; 47 (2003): 71- 87.

**EUROPOEM – The development, maintenance and dissemination of a European predictive operator exposure model.** TNO, The Netherlands.

**Legislative and preventive measures related to contact dermatitis**. C Liden. Contact Dermatitis; 44 (2001): 65-69.

**General best shop practices. Design for the environment**. www.epa.gov

**Let's dispel a few myths. Bad Hand Days**. www.badhandday.hse.gov.uk

**Principles of sensible risk management.** Health and Safety Executive, London, UK. http://www.hse.gov.uk/risk/principles

**Protecting workers from dermal exposure – The German experience.** E Lechtenberg-Auffarth, B Orthen. Federal Institute of Occupational Safety and Health, Dortmund, Germany.

**Preventing contact dermatitis at work**. INDG233(rev1). Health and Safety Executive, London, UK.

**Prevention of skin and respiratory problems among hairdressers**. J Terwoert, HB van der Walle, B Hol. Centre of Skin and Occupation, Arnhem, Netherlands.

**Public Register of Enforcement Notices.** Health and Safety Executive, London, UK. www.hse.gov.uk/notices

**Rash Decisions: HSE video.** Health and Safety Executive. London, UK.

**Task-based dermal exposure models for regulatory risk assessment.** ND Warren, H Marquart, Y Christopher, J Laitinen, JJ Van Hemmen. Annals of Occupational Hygiene; 50 (2006): 491-503.

**Topic Inspection Pack – Work-Related Contact Dermatitis.** Health and Safety Executive, London, UK . www.hse.gov.uk

# Chapter 10

# Avoiding Contact with the Skin

An employer's first and foremost legal duty is to prevent employees' exposure to *hazardous substances* by all routes. They should establish whether it is *reasonably practicable* to prevent the exposure by measures other than the use of personal protective equipment (PPE). Where a decision is made that it is not reasonably practicable to prevent exposure, it must be adequately controlled.

This Chapter deals with the "avoid contact with the skin" part of the APC approach described in Chapter 9 and describes examples of measures for preventing or adequately controlling dermal exposure to chemicals and *wet-work*. These examples are intended to encourage readers to develop control solutions for other exposure scenarios.

## PREVENTION OF EXPOSURE

The need to prevent exposure is not a new approach. The ancient Romans and Cornish tin miners had common sense systems in place for preventing exposure.

Romans designed their lavatory system in such way as to prevent hand contamination. To achieve the desired results, they put in place a soft brush attached to a handle. During use, the brush would be dipped into a stream of clean running water. In this example, the requirement for adequate safe working distance (SWD) was achieved with the handled brush.

Cornish tin miners were exposed to lead, arsenic and other heavy metals. This exposure occurred via skin contact, inhalation and ingestion. The legend goes that ingestion route due to hand contamination was a concern for the wives of Cornish miners. This concern led to the invention of the world famous Cornish pasty. The original Cornish pasty had two halves, one half contained the main meal and the other half contained the sweet. The pasty had a large folded area (the crust), also, providing a

SWD. When consuming the food, the pasty was held by the folded area.

These two examples show that sensible Dermal Exposure Risk Management (DERM) does not always have to involve expensive high-tech solutions. Simple but effective approaches can be applied for preventing skin exposure to hazardous substances. Several more examples are described below.

## A. Eliminating Completely the Use of Hazardous Substances

Heavy structures like cranes and bridges were historically coated with red-lead (lead oxide) paints to protect them from corrosion damage. During maintenance (e.g. application of paint and blast cleaning) and disposal (e.g. flame cutting and burning) of these structures, many workers were exposed (by all routes) to significant amounts of lead, which can cause damage to various organs.

In this case, it is reasonably practicable to eliminate the use of this hazardous substance. It was achieved by using alternative protective techniques, such as zinc galvanising and anodic protection in which another easily corroding material is welded to the structure as a sacrificial protector, and the application of unleaded protective coatings. The elimination of red-lead paints resulted in significant reduction in lead exposure related occupational diseases. It also prevented lead contamination lodged in clothing reaching homes.

Another example is the elimination of organic-lead additives in petrol. This helped to prevent lead exposure among production workers, fuel producers, fuel handlers, tanker drivers, vehicle repairers and dismantlers.

## B. Changing the Method of Work so that the Activity or Task Presenting the Potential for Exposure is no Longer Necessary

Epoxy resins are known to cause allergic contact dermatitis (ACD). However, these resins are essential part of the modern day technology and life. They are used widely in the construction industry for a variety of applications. Workers' skin often come into contact with these substances when two parts of the resin (accelerator and adhesive) are mixed together to prepare the working resin. An example is shown in Figure 10.1. There are many practicable approaches for minimising skin contact and these include: (i) using pierceable epoxy kits with well-defined mixing ratios (Figure 10.2); (ii) using dual package kits which do not require weighing (Figure 10.3); and (iii) using dual syringe systems, (Figure 10.4), where only small amounts are required at any one time.

**Figure 10.1** This picture shows surface contamination and the potential for splashing from manual weighing, transferring and mixing of epoxy resins and hardeners. *Photograph: Courtesy of the European Epoxy Project Team and IVAM, Amsterdam, The Netherlands.*

**Figure 10.2** A semi-automated mixing system. A defined mixing ratio is established at the manufacturing plant. The hardener can be added, when needed, by piercing the blue band. The resulting aperture allows mixing to take place in the container. *Photograph: Courtesy of the European Epoxy Project Team and IVAM, Amsterdam, The Netherlands.*

## C.  Substituting Hazardous Substances with Non-Hazardous Substances

Solvents are commonly used for removing crusted carbon, corrosion products and paints from jet engines. It is reasonably practicable to use alternative techniques not requiring the use of solvents. One such technique uses dry carbon dioxide for blast cleaning the engines. When this technique is employed, work systems in place should include measures to prevent the potential for asphyxiation.

## D. Modifying a Process to Eliminate the Production of a Hazardous By-Product or Waste Product

In the past, polychlorinated biphenyls (PCBs) were used as thermal insulators in power generating and voltage reduction transformers. PCBs are a danger to the skin and other parts of the body and cause long-term damage to the natural environment including animals. The process was redesigned to eliminate the use of PCBs, which in turn eliminated the exposure among production, dismantling and disposal workers. In addition, the environment benefited significantly from this changeover.

**Figure 10.3** Dual package epoxy kits requiring no weighing of hardeners and adhesives. These systems are designed by pre-calculation and are useful when a 2-10kg epoxy mix is needed at any one time. *Photograph: Courtesy of the European Epoxy Project Team and IVAM, Amsterdam, The Netherlands.*

**Figure 10.4:** When a small amount of a resin mix is needed at any one time, a dual syringe system could be used. System **A** is used with a purpose designed dispenser. **B** shows a plastic syringe based system. These systems can be transported safely from one workplace to another and the required amount of adhesive can be mixed on demand. Peripatetic workers will find these useful.

## E. Using a Different form of the Same Substance for Preventing Exposure

Enzyme-based detergents are in common use in many homes and industrial sectors. Following their introduction in the 60s, it was discovered that exposure to the enzymes caused sensitisation cases among workers in factories formulating and packaging detergents and among users at home. One of the major reasons was the use of finely powdered enzymes. In this form, they readily become airborne during various handling processes, causing skin and inhalation exposure. Dusts settling on surfaces and clothing caused secondary exposures. In order to deal with this problem, the industry reformulated the enzymes from fine powders into encapsulated granules. This modification led to a significant reduction in sensitisation among the workers.

## F. Using an Alternative Less Hazardous Substance

Hexavalent chromium (Cr (VI)) compounds are used for dip coating and electrolytic plating of metal articles. It is considered that exposure via the skin, inhalation or by ingestion carries an increased risk of cancer. In addition, Cr (VI) is a skin sensitiser. Regulatory pressures, however, have forced the industry to switch to Cr (III) for many applications. This switch over is expected to deliver long term health benefits to those employed in the metal coating and other surface finishing sectors.

## G. Using a Different Process

Methylene chloride (dichloromethane or DCM) is used extensively as a paint stripper and the work activity causes significant dermal and inhalation exposures among the painters. Research showed that this substance could be substituted with products based on esters, but they are not as effective as DCM. Nevertheless, a limited changeover can deliver benefits to workers and the environment.

## H. Application of prevention and control

This may be explained in the context of brick laying, which involves manual handling of bricks and wet cement. The activity can cause skin exposure to chromium-containing wet cement, providing a potential for ACD. Technological advances and low production costs have made it practicable to use chromium-free cement. However, it is not reasonably practicable to prevent the use of wet cement or to automate the process (at present) at a building site. Therefore, significant risk reduction measures include the use of suitable gloves and skin care products.

### ADEQUATE CONTROL OF EXPOSURE

The application of the 'good control practices', as explained in Chapter 5, should control skin exposure to hazardous substances. When implementing good control practices, employers should take account of human factors and ergonomic principles. In addition, systems should be in place to deal with accidents and emergencies. Examples in this section will describe different approaches for achieving adequate control.

### Safe Working Distance

To achieve adequate control of skin exposure, in particular to the hands, it is necessary to develop and use adequate SWD between the hands and hazardous substances. SWD can be put in place in various ways. A poster published by the Health and Safety Executive (HSE) and reprinted in Figure 3.4, illustrates the application of SWD.

## A. Totally Enclosing the Process

Total enclosure should help to create a SWD between the individual, the process and the hazardous substance used in the process. A typical example is a fully enclosed, ventilated and computer automated metal turning lathe. Raw materials to be machined are fed automatically; turned parts are automatically collected in a tray and transferred for laundering to remove excess burrs and oil. The application of the metal working fluid is managed by the same computer.

## B. Totally Enclosing the Handling System

Solvent handling and transferring are common tasks in many industrial processes. Activities such as those shown in Figures 10.5 and 2.5 can create many opportunities for dermal exposure, but the exposure can be minimised by improved handling and transfer methods. An example transfer system is shown Figure 10.6. It has a concealed dip pipe within an outer sheath. The concealed pipe can be lowered into a solvent container by opening the release valve, after that the solvent can be transferred to the working container through the transfer pipe. Once the transfer is complete or when the solvent container is empty, the contaminated dip pipe can be safely retracted back into its housing and sealed via the valve. This type of transfer system will help to reduce exposure via the skin and inhalation.

**Figure 10.5** Solvent dispensing with a system similar to a petrol dispenser. This system was used for transferring considerable quantities of toluene several times each day. Poorly designed control systems provide opportunities for evaporation, splashing and contamination of the skin, clothing and surfaces. In addition, the practices will contribute to significant inhalation exposure. A poorly designed LEV system is in the background.

**Figure 10.6**

This figure shows systems designed for safe ways to transfer hazardous liquids. They are designed to prevent contact with hazardous chemicals during and after transfer.

**A** – shows a system in rest position. In this position, the dip tube is safely held inside the vertical blue sleeve. During use, the dip tube will be released into the container and the sleeve will be seated on top of the drum as shown in B.

**B** – Any vapour in the sleeve will be captured by the local exhaust ventilation system connected to the sleeve (silver piping).

**C** – shows other types of solvent transfer systems and the operator is kitted with chemical protective coverall and respiratory protection in case of control failure during transfer. Photographs A and B: Courtesy of the Control Transfer Technology Ltd. (CTTL), Newcastle upon Tyne, Tyne and Wear, UK. Photograph C: Courtesy of DuPont Engineering Products s.a.r.l, L-2984, Luxembourg.

### C. Partial Enclosure with Local Exhaust Ventilation

Surface finishing is an important and essential activity in many industrial production processes and may involve components of different sizes and shapes. The surface treatment could be undertaken in a partial enclosure with the help of a rotating turntable (Figure 10.7). In this example, the switch to initiate the rotation is underneath the table. An improved system would include a foot operated switch and a suitable mechanical or manual hook for transferring articles. These improvements will help to increase productivity and reduce the potential for back injuries and skin exposure. In addition, the spray table and the immediate floor area may be covered with disposable paper sheets to enable easy cleaning and disposal of the overspray waste. The water wash system reduces the need for regular cleaning of the enclosure surfaces and facilitates automated removal of waste. The potential for contamination of the compressed air supply tube may be avoided by covering it with a polyethylene sleeve, which can be removed once the paint is cured.

### D. Providing Adequate and Suitable Local Exhaust Ventilation System

Local exhaust ventilation (LEV) systems are designed for capturing airborne contaminants. A cursory examination of the outer surfaces of many systems (e.g. outside surfaces of ventilation hoods and trunks) and the surfaces around the hood will provide evidence of their ineffectiveness and/or how good the work practices are. A typical ineffective LEV is shown in Figure 10.8. This system was designed to control methylene bischloroaniline (MbOCA) dust and vapour. It is clear from the positions of the extraction slots that the system is unlikely to extract the dust and vapour effectively. The dust and vapour escaping into the work area can contribute to skin and surface contamination. MbOCA on surfaces can cause skin, ingestion and inhalation exposures. It is important to design, install, maintain and correctly use LEV systems for achieving adequate exposure control by all routes.

### E. Changes to Work Including Handling Systems

If workers are asked: "Why are you doing this work in this way?" Often the answer will be: "That is the way we have always done it." Where a long-established procedure is in place, employers may not appreciate the dangers associated with exposure to hazardous substances. Examples used in this section will illustrate that it is often easy to make modifications to work systems and the changes can lead to significant reductions in exposure by all routes.

Common practices involved in the application of epoxy floor coatings are shown in Figure 10.9. These pictures show that work methods have the potential to cause contamination of the skin, gloves and clothing. However, it is easy to apply simple control methods and two examples are shown in Figure 10.10. The modifications used will not only help to minimise skin exposure, it will also help to reduce the potential for back injuries and manual handling problems.

Figure 6.3 shows a person dip coating a work piece and the hands are being used as a tool. This is not necessary. A simple 'S' hook could be used for dipping, lifting and draining the excess coat. In a large scale production, coating processes could be automated in many ways and an example is shown in Figure 10.11.

Figures 10.12 and 10.13 are showing workers using either a solvent-soaked rag or bare hands for cleaning tasks. A tool similar to the one shown in Figure 10.14 could be adopted to make the jobs easier and to establish suitable SWD. Modified work practices should help to reduce contamination of gloves and work surfaces including the switches on machines. Modifications to work practices should help to reduce the potential for skin contamination and inhalation exposure caused by contaminated clothing, gloves and hands.

## F. Process Changes

Kitchen equipment contaminated with cooking grease can be cleaned using sodium hydroxide solution, a caustic substance, which can cause severe burns to the skin. In order to prevent the use of the solution, sodium hydroxide could be applied using a foam matrix (Figure 10.15). The excess foam and the dissolved grease could be wiped off with a tool similar to the one shown in Figure 10.14.

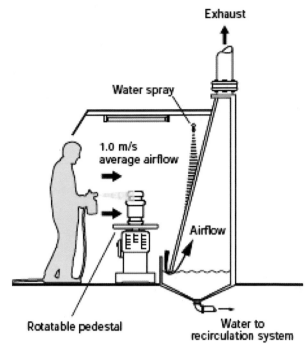

m/s = metres per second

**Figure 10.7** A spray booth with a table containing a rotating pedestal for placing items to be sprayed. The switch for the pedestal is underneath the platform. This is not ideal. An improved approach will incorporate a foot switch. This improved ergonomic design will help to prevent contamination of the skin and switch and the temptation for hand manipulation of the pedestal and contaminated articles.

**Figure 10.8:** An ineffective local exhaust ventilation (LEV) system. The designer of the LEV opted for a flexible ducting and a three quarter slot at the end. The designer's intentions are good. However, the flexible hood arrangement lacks suitable handles for manipulating the arrangement. Operators failed to place the slot close to the "cooking" containers on the work bench.

The arrangement failed to control surface contamination and vapour escape into work area. An alternative slot design (e.g. three quarter slot fixed at the back or a push-pull lip extraction arrangement across the bench) would enable effective use of the LEV.

**Figure 10.9:** These pictures show that the processes and work practices are employing some degree of safe working distance (SWD). They can be improved significantly in many ways. Examples are shown in Fig. 10.10. Photographs: *Courtesy of the European Epoxy Team and IVAM, Amsterdam, The Netherlands.*

**Figures 10.10**

**A** – shows epoxy mix being poured using an easy to use facility rather than carrying a bucket full of epoxy resin and pouring with hands.

**B** – shows epoxy mix being spread with the help of a long handled spreader providing an adequate safe working distance (SWD). If a short handled spreader is used, the operator will have to kneel down (see Fig. 10.9) presenting a significant potential for dermal exposure and back problems.

*Photographs: Courtesy of the European Epoxy Project Team and IVAM, Amsterdam, The Netherlands.*

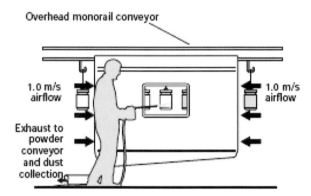

**Figure 10.11** A large scale surface coating process. The product to be coated moves on a line and the surface coating is applied using a spray gun with a deflector pad in front of the operator. Coated product can go through the curing process without the need for manual handling of wet products. The items are hung on hooks, making the handling process simpler. The operator is using an adequate safe working distance (SWD) to minimise skin exposure.

**Figure 10.13** The operator is cleaning used print rollers and accessories. His hands are in direct contact with solvent contaminated surfaces. Solvent soaked rags and toilet tissues were used for cleaning and drying. The work surfaces and the walls have been contaminated. Breathing zone sampling will not provide information on skin exposure, which is the major exposure route. Skin exposure to solvents can contribute to skin uptake.

**Figure 10.14** An example of a cleaning sponge mounted on a handle to provide a safe working distance (SWD). A device similar to this could be used or designed for cleaning print plates and rollers. It is a better option than using solvent soaked rags.

**Figure 10.12** The operator used a solvent soaked rag for cleaning printing machines. Efforts should be directed to finding alternative approaches providing adequate safe working distance (SWD) between the hands and solvents. The picture shows a wet rag and a gloved hand resting on a cabinet.

**Figure 10.15**

An oven cleaning chemical, based on sodium hydroxide, is encapsulated in a foam matrix to minimise skin and inhalation exposure during use. Sodium hydroxide is a corrosive substance and can cause severe burns to the skin and respiratory system.

## G. Administrative Controls

An office worker in an electrical components manufacturing company developed a skin rash, especially on the face. Investigation showed that the problem was due to exposure to rosin. The exposure took place when the office worker issued daily worksheets directly to the employees in workshops where soldering took place. Procedures were modified to prevent the worker visiting the workshops and minimise contamination of the paperwork. Following the implementation of the new procedures, the worker's condition improved because the exposure was minimised.

An experienced nursing Sister in a gastro-enterology ward developed an allergic reaction to single-use powdered latex gloves. This situation created a requirement for sensible risk management system because (i) the employer did not want to lose an experienced member of staff to another department and (ii) they had responsibilities under health and safety and disability discrimination laws. They found that for a majority of procedures, there was no need to use powdered single-use latex gloves. It was established that it was reasonably practicable to use disposable powder-free nitrile gloves. A system was set up to provide good quality nitrile gloves. In addition, staff members, in the department, were instructed that powdered latex gloves should only be used for a valid reason and the Sister in question should be excluded from the area when the gloves were used. The new procedure enabled the Sister to carry on working in the department.

A trade union safety representative received a complaint from a member of his union that the employer was asking him to wash his contaminated coveralls at home. The work involved stone grinding and cutting, which created silica dust. The safety representative was aware that the coveralls were likely to be contaminated with silica dust including crystalline silica. So, he took the matter to the employer and explained the risks involved, including the potential for the employee's family members being exposed to the dust. The safety representative also explained that the employer has a duty to provide suitable and clean PPE free of charge and take reasonable steps to prevent people outside work being exposed to hazardous substances created at work. Having recognised the risks and the need to comply with the law, the employer reinstated the previous practice of professional cleaning.

## H. Using Suitable Personal Protective Equipment

A construction company failed to identify the hazards associated with wet cement or provide employees with suitable information, training and PPE. One of the workers suffered cement burns to his knees simply because he was not wearing suitable knee pads (Figure 2.2). The company was fined £15,000 and ordered to pay £7000 costs.

Hairdressers, in general, have been reluctant to use gloves for shampooing and rinsing clients' hair. They have argued that gloves may snag customers' hair or they may scald customers' skin simply because they will not be able to feel the temperature of the water when wearing gloves. These are genuine behavioural issues and need solutions. It was explained that a thin, all-round smooth, close fitting glove with no folds would help to overcome the problems and these were demonstrated by experiments and user surveys. This approach helped to increase the extent of gloves use, which should help to minimise irritant contact dermatitis due to wet-work.

## CONCLUSION

Prevention is better than cure. If it is not reasonably practicable to prevent skin exposure to chemicals and wet-work, adequate control measures should be put in place. This Chapter provides practical advice and examples of approaches for prevention and/or control of exposure. They should help readers to develop suitable exposure control solutions in their workplaces. Many of the examples illustrate the implementation of adequate SWD between the skin and chemicals. LEV systems should be designed to minimise inhalation and skin exposure. Pictures and diagrams are useful tools for effective risk communication and management.

## TEST YOUR KNOWLEDGE

1. Do you think skin exposure can lead to inhalation exposure? Why?

2. Do you consider that third parties outside the immediate work environment could be exposed to hazardous substances? Explain why?

3. Carry out a walk through survey of your workplace and identify whether skin exposure could be controlled by means other than PPE and what approaches could be used for establishing adequate SWD.

## FURTHER READING

**Assessing and managing risks at work from skin exposure to chemical agents (HSG 205).** HSE Books, Sudbury, UK. ISBN 0 7176 1826 9.

**Come clean about solvents.**
C Atkins. Health and Safety at Work; 26 (2004): 14-16.

**Control of substances hazardous to health (Fifth edition).**
HSE Books, Sudbury, UK. ISBN 0 7176 2981 3.

**Controlling skin diseases when handling epoxy resins.**
European Agency for Safety and Health at Work. www.osha.eu.int

COSHH Essentials. www.cossh-essentails.org

**Essentials of Occupational Skin Management**. CL Packham. Limited Edition Press, Southport, UK. ISBN 1 85988 045 2.

**European Directive on Cement (2003/53.EC)**.
Official Journal of the European Union. L178/24. 17.7.2003.

**Let's dispel a few myths.** Bad Hand Days.
www.badhandday.hse.gov.uk

**Man didn't feel cement burning his knees.**
Safety Management (British Safety Council); September 2006.

**Prevent Work-Related Dermatitis. It's in Your Hands.**
© bsif.virgin.co.uk

**Reducing the risks of ill-health from hexavalent chromium compounds in the electroplating industry**. Sector Information Minute (SIM03/2005/16). Health and Safety Executive, UK. www.hse.gov.uk

**Save Our Skin**. BR Sithamparanadarajah D Llewellyn. Safety Management (British Safety Council); December 2007. .

*Chapter 11*

# Protecting the Skin with PPE

## INTRODUCTION

Personal protective equipment (PPE) falls within the second aspect (protect the skin), of the APC approach described in Chapter 9. Where a combined application of process, engineering and administrative controls do not deliver *adequate control* of exposure, employers should provide adequate and suitable PPE to further reduce the exposure. Employers spend thousands of pounds a year on the purchase of gloves and clothing to protect against chemicals. Some employees use hundreds of pairs of gloves every year to protect their hands. However, a considerable number of PPE users do not achieve the expected level of protection for a variety of reasons. This is not a satisfactory situation and this Chapter will describe practical approaches for the correct selection and use of chemical protective gloves and clothing.

## PERSONAL PROTECTIVE EQUIPMENT

The term personal protective equipment or PPE may be used to represent many types of devices, clothing, gloves and appliances. How it is defined varies from one country to another. Similarly the requirements for design, testing and approval of PPE will depend on the regulatory systems in force. In this book, the legal framework is explained in the context of the European system.

### What is PPE?

In the European system, for a device, clothing, glove or an appliance to be defined as PPE, it must satisfy two criteria:

(i)   It is to be worn on any part of the body or held by a person at work <u>and</u>

(ii)  It is designed to protect that person against one or more health and/or safety hazards.

The above definition of PPE will also include:

● A protective unit manufactured by combining several devices. For example, an ensemble, consisting of respiratory protective equipment (RPE), gloves and a coverall with integrated foot protection, designed and intended to be used together will fall in this category;

● A protective element manufactured in combination with another device. A typical example is the high visibility element incorporated into a raincoat; and

● Interchangeable components that are essential to the satisfactory functioning of a PPE device or appliance and is used exclusively with a given type of device or appliance. A particulate filter used with a reusable half mask RPE will fall into this category.

Before PPE can be placed on the market by its manufacturer or supplier, it should meet the minimum health, safety, design and quality standards applicable to that type and should have undergone conformity assessment.

### Categories of PPE

There are three categories of PPE and these are:

● Category I (for use against minimal or minor risks)

PPE in this category is known as 'simple design' offering protection from low levels of risks. In this case, the risks presented by the hazard are gradual in nature and the PPE wearer should be able to safely identify the hazards and risks in good time. Gloves made for gardening will fall within this category. The manufacturer of this type of PPE is permitted to test for performance, certify and "CE" mark the PPE themselves.

● Category II (for use against intermediate or reversible risks)

Any PPE that does not fit the requirements of Categories I and III is placed in this category. PPE in this category must be subjected to testing and certification by an authorised independent body set up for this purpose under the European legislation. The 'CE' mark can only be put on the PPE when it has passed scrutiny by the approved independent body. A general purpose glove requiring cut or puncture resistance might fall into this category.

- Category III (for use against mortal or irreversible risks)

PPE in this category is known as 'complex design' and is intended to protect against severe hazards that can cause serious and irreversible harm to the health and safety of the PPE wearer. It is considered that the user cannot identify the harm, (e.g. dermatitis, burns and cancer caused by chemicals), in sufficient time to take protective action. PPE placed in this category must be subjected to the same level of independent testing and certification as Category II PPE, but in addition is subjected to continuing assurance of the quality of the product through either periodic testing of samples or by adherence to a quality assurance scheme. The nature of the hazard (e.g. protection against chemical ***permeation***) which the PPE is intended to protect against must be clearly stated.

## CE Marking

PPE satisfying the basic health and safety requirements of the PPE Directive is considered safe to be sold in Europe, and can be identified by the presence of a 'CE' mark and other relevant information.

However, PPE meeting the basic health and safety requirements of the Directive and stamped with a 'CE' mark does not automatically become suitable for use at work. The selection of adequate and suitable PPE, ensuring its correct use and maintenance is the responsibility of the employer.

## Product Markings and Pictograms

The type of markings, pictograms and performance information provided with a particular PPE will vary according to the hazard(s) for which it is designed, tested and certified. Tables 11.1 – 11.3 describe the pictograms and markings relevant to gloves.

## What is not PPE?

Some devices worn or held by a person at work are not PPE because they do not satisfy the PPE definition described earlier. Gloves used for protecting patients or food hygiene requirements are not PPE. The former is certified under medical devices regulations and the latter is certified under food hygiene regulations. These gloves are intended to protect the patient or the product from the wearer, and not *vice-versa*. However, these devices can also carry the 'CE' mark. By now, it should be clear that a 'CE' mark on its own cannot be relied upon to determine whether a device is PPE or not. Most importantly 'CE' mark cannot, on its own, be taken as an indication of adequacy and suitability during PPE assessments.

**Table 11.1** Pictograms, chemical hazards, Standards and performance for gloves

| Pictogram | Hazard | European Standard | Performance description | Performance ranking (higher the number better the performance) |
|---|---|---|---|---|
| | Chemical permeation **and** Chemical penetration | EN 374 | Permeation performance and breakthrough time (min). Tested with at least 3 specified chemicals (one at a time) to EN 374-3 | 1 > 10 min 2 > 30 min 3 > 60 min 4 > 120 min 5 > 240 min 6 > 480 min |
| | | | Penetration. Freedom from holes to EN 374-2. Air or water leak test | 1 – AQLA < 4% 2 – AQL < 1.5% 3 – AQL < 0.65% |
| | Chemical penetration **only** | EN 374 | Penetration. Freedom from holes to EN 374-2. Air or water leak test | 1 – AQLA < 4% 2 – AQL < 1.5% 3 – AQL < 0.65% |
| | Micro-organisms | EN 374-2 | Penetration. Freedom from holes to EN 374-2. Air or water leak test | At least level 2 performance |

*Note: A - AQL = Acceptance quality level for batch production, roughly equates to the percentage of product which may contain holes*

Furthermore, the European PPE law excludes the following:

- PPE specifically designed for armed forces or used in the maintenance of law and order;

- PPE designed for private use against adverse atmospheric conditions (e.g. seasonal clothing, footwear and umbrellas); damp and water (e.g. household gloves); and

**Table 11.2** Pictograms, mechanical hazards, Standards and performance for gloves

| Pictogram | Hazard | European Standard | Performance description | Performance ranking (higher the number better the performance) |
|---|---|---|---|---|
| | Mechanical | EN 388 | a – Abrasion resistance<br>b – Blade resistance<br>c – Tear resistance<br>d – Puncture resistance | 0 – 4<br>0 – 5<br>0 – 4<br>0 – 4<br><br>(0 – fail or not tested) |
| | Mechanical | EN 388 | Impact cut resistance | Pass or fail |
| No pictogram. (a weakness of EN Standards) | Mechanical | EN 420 | Dexterity. Ability to pick up specified size pins between the gloved forefinger and the thumb. (see right column) | 1 (11mm)<br>2 (9.5 mm)<br>3 (8 mm)<br>4 (6.5 mm)<br>5 (5 mm) |

**Table 11.3** Pictograms, thermal hazards, Standards and performance for gloves

| Pictogram | Hazard | European Standard | Performance description | Performance ranking (higher the number better the performance) |
|---|---|---|---|---|
| | Cold | EN 511 | a – Resistance to convective cold<br>b – Resistance to contact cold<br>c – Permeability to water | a – 1 to 4<br><br>b – 1 to 4<br><br>c – 1 if water permeable |
| | Flammability and heat | EN 407 | a – burning resistance<br>b – contact heat resistance<br>c – convective heat resistance<br>d – radiant heat resistance<br>e – resistance to small splashes of molten metal<br>f – resistance to large splashes of molten metal | Each requirement to 1 to 4 |

- PPE intended for protection or rescue on ships, boats and aircraft that are not worn all the time (e.g. life vests).

## Why is PPE the Last Resort?

Health and safety laws prescribe that PPE, including chemical protective gloves and coveralls, is the last line of protection. The reasons for this include:

- PPE can only protect the wearer. Control measures at source protect all those in the area, including people not at work;

- If the PPE is sized, selected or used incorrectly, or is badly maintained, the wearer is unlikely to receive adequate protection;

- PPE is uncomfortable to wear and is an intrusion into normal activities;

- PPE may interfere with the work. The interference may be due to factors such as incorrect size, incorrect length, inappropriate shape, inappropriate thickness (causing loss of dexterity) and incompatible material from which PPE is made;

- Contaminated PPE may present one or more risks to the wearer and third parties such as waste handlers and family members. In the case of family members, risk arises when the contaminated PPE is taken home.

- The extent of protection achieved depends on good fit and attention to detail.

When PPE is used as the last resort, it is the last line of defence between the user and the harm. If it does not work for any reason, the user will be exposed to the hazard. This is why PPE must be selected, used, maintained and stored correctly.

## REQUIREMENTS TO PROVIDE PPE

### Applicable Situations

The situations where employers are required to provide PPE for dermal exposure protection include:

- Where dermal exposure risks remain (residual risk) even after implementing *reasonably practicable* controls at source (e.g. process, engineering and administrative) to ensure adequate safe working distance (SWD) between the chemicals and the skin;

- Short-term or infrequent dermal exposures where implementing controls at source to establish suitable SWD is not reasonably practicable;

- As an interim measure, while other control measures are being put in place to achieve adequate dermal exposure control;

- For dealing with emergency work that cannot wait until suitable controls at source are put in place;

- To deal with temporary failure of control where other means of controls are not reasonably practical;

- Emergency rescue by trained personnel.

However, there may be circumstances where an employer may consider it to be prudent to issue PPE, not because other control measures are inadequate on their own, but to provide protection in case those control measures fail to operate. Where this approach is considered, the wearers should be informed and the PPE should be subjected to the normal selection, use and maintenance requirements and should meet the adequacy and suitability requirements.

### PPE and Charges

An employer cannot demand money from an employee for PPE, even in the form of a returnable deposit. However, the PPE remains the property of the employer. This requirement will also apply to agency workers, if they are legally regarded, for health and safety purposes, as employees at the place of employment.

## WHAT IS ADEQUATE AND SUITABLE PPE?

### Adequate PPE

PPE is considered adequate if it can provide the necessary 'level of protection' against the hazard so as to comply with the law. For example, a chemical protective glove chosen for protection against solvents should not degrade during use and cause exposure; hazardous substances should not contaminate the insides of the gloves; where Biological Monitoring Guidance Values (BMGV) exist, the combined protective measures, (gloves and other protective measures), should help to ensure that relevant BMGV is not exceeded (more information is in Chapter 8); another approach would be to compare the dermal exposure monitoring results against the values for "total daily dermal contamination giving cause for concern" (Table 8.2).

### Suitable PPE

PPE is considered suitable if it is adequate against the hazard and matched to the wearer, the task, and the workplace conditions, such that the wearer can work with minimum impediment and without additional risks due to the PPE.

## CHEMICAL PROTECTIVE GLOVES

Exposure of the hands to chemicals is an important and significant contributor to total skin exposure. It has been shown that the exposure of the hands accounts for between 50 and 90% of total skin exposure. To mitigate this problem, it is common practice to provide gloves rather than establishing adequate SWD between the skin and the contaminants by other measures. This could be the reason that chemical protective gloves are one of the most widely used forms of PPE. Gloves are used for providing localised protection to the skin from irritant, allergic and corrosive substances and/or protection against chemical uptake through the skin.

## Factors Affecting the Performance of Chemical Protective Gloves

### Glove Factors

There is a wide range of chemical protective gloves on the market and they vary in design, quality and performance. No glove or combination of glove materials will be capable of providing unlimited resistance to any individual chemicals or mixture of chemicals. The main reason is the intrinsic (in-built) properties of glove materials, such as permeation and dissolution at molecular level leading to permeation breakthrough, swelling and disintegration. Therefore, it is essential to have a basic understanding of the major intrinsic (in-built) failure mechanisms so that sensible approaches can be taken for the correct selection and use of suitable gloves. In addition, this knowledge can be used for dispelling myths that chemical protective gloves can provide complete and unlimited protection from all chemicals.

### Intrinsic Failure Mechanisms

There are three major intrinsic mechanisms by which any chemical protective glove will, at some stage, fail to protect the wearer from exposure to chemicals. These are:

● Permeation;

● Penetration; and

● Degradation.

### Permeation

Permeation is the process by which a chemical moves through the protective glove material at molecular level. Once the outer surface of a glove material comes into contact with a chemical, the molecules of the chemical will be absorbed onto the surface of the glove material. As soon as this happens, the process leading to permeation breakthrough will start. It takes place in three stages and is shown in diagrammatic form in Figure 11.1.

Absorption is the taking up of the molecules of a chemical by the glove material. This takes place once the molecules of the chemical come into contact with the surface of the glove material.

Diffusion is the movement of the chemical molecules from the high concentration side of the glove to the lower concentration side. The rate of diffusion is mainly dependant on the concentration gradient, molecular size and the molecular weight of the chemical, temperature

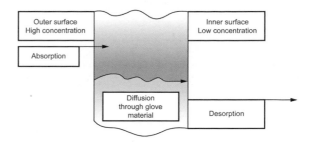

**Figure 11.1** An illustration of permeation breakthrough process. Solvent molecules, on the outside surface of a glove, diffuse through the minute spaces present in the molecular arrangement of the glove material and end up at the inside surface of the glove (i.e. the side in contact with the skin when worn.)

and the glove material. For example, a molecule four times larger than another will move half as fast through the glove material. In other words, lower molecular weight substances, like acetone, will permeate through a nitrile glove much faster than will mineral oil, which has a much larger molecular weight.

Desorption is the liberation of the molecules of a chemical from the glove material at the low concentration side. When this happens, permeation breakthrough is considered to have occurred.

Because of the molecular level process, permeation of a chemical through glove materials goes unnoticed by the wearers. The permeated chemical will present itself as vapour in between the inside surface of the glove material and the skin in contact with the glove material. Once the process of permeation has begun, it will continue even if the glove material is no longer exposed to the chemical (e.g. during storage). Permeation will stop only when the chemical has completely desorbed from the glove material. Example plots of permeation breakthrough time monitoring are shown in Figure 11.2.

Permeation breakthrough times provided by glove manufacturers are specific to the product to which it refers and based on laboratory test data. These tests are normally based on standard test methods published in Standards such as EN374, ASTM F 739 and ISO 6529. In Europe, the test data is expressed in various ways as shown in Tables 11.4a and b.

### Permeation and Gloves Selection

As a general rule, manufacturers' permeation breakthrough times should not be used for the selection of adequate and suitable gloves for three main reasons:

(i)  Laboratory permeation breakthrough times are obtained by challenging glove material with a single chemical rather than a mixture of chemicals as found in real workplaces;

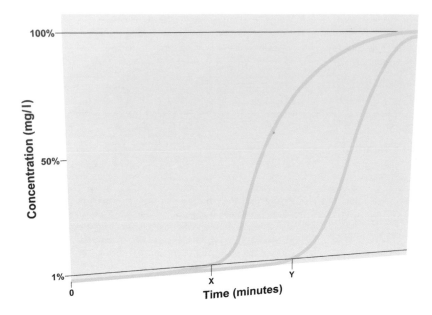

**Figure 11.2** Permeation breakthrough curve.

Substance X has a short breakthrough time compared to substance Y. Chemical protective gloves should be subjected to permeation testing using chemicals recommended in relevant Standards.

Permeation breakthrough time is established, when a specified amount (e.g. $1\mu g/cm^2$) of the test chemical has broken through the glove material under specified test conditions.

Permeation breakthrough time is one of the classification parameters for assessing the potential performance of chemical protective gloves and these are given in Tables 11.4a and 11.4b.

(ii) The data is obtained without flexing and stretching of the glove material; and

(iii) The test is conducted at about 23°C. This temperature is not representative of the hands, and permeation breakthrough times at 35°C can be significantly faster for glove/chemical combination, as shown in Table 11.5.

The Health and Safety Executive (HSE) recommends that *"as a general rule, glove protection levels published by the manufacturers can be reduced by up to 75% when the gloves are in active use. If you need protection from exposure to particularly aggressive or harmful chemicals, you should take this safety factor into account when selecting gloves."* The outcome of this advice translates as follows in the following example: a manufacturer's data shows that the glove can be used for up to 480 minutes against phenol; however, by taking account of the HSE advice, the glove should not be used for more than 120 minutes. The application of HSE's recommendation may be too cautious because strong theoretical and experimental arguments are emerging to suggest that the correction factor recommended may be too conservative. Calculations have been put forward to show that actual dermal uptake is likely to be much lower than that suggested on the basis of permeation breakthrough concentrations (see "Protective gloves for occupational use" listed in the further reading section). The knowledge in this area is developing and it will take time to establish a coherent way forward.

In the meantime, a number of practical measures could be put in place to minimise the effects from permeation breakthrough. These include:

● Preventing immersion of hands (with or without gloves) into solvents and other chemicals;

● Establishing adequate SWD by means other than the use of gloves;

● Wiping off as soon as is practical any solvents in contact with the outer surfaces of gloves. This precaution should help to reduce the amount of chemical reaching the insides of the glove because of a significantly reduced concentration gradient.

● Where it is not reasonably practical to avoid immersion, splash resistant single-use gloves should be used.

● For reusable gloves, a safety factor of 0.5 could be applied to the permeation breakthrough times provided by glove manufacturers, unless they are able to provide test data applicable to your chemical mixtures and the workplace situation.

● When gloves are not in use, they should be stored in such a way that the insides of the gloves can be naturally aired.

● Discarding any gloves that have become soft, swollen, shrunk or stiffened during use.

**Table 11.4a** Approaches for expressing permeation data

| Measured breakthrough time (min) | Protection class/index/levels |
|---|---|
| >10 | 1 |
| >30 | 2 |
| >60 | 3 |
| >120 | 4 |
| >240 | 5 |
| >480 | 6 |

**Table 11.4b** Alternative approaches for expressing permeation data

| Permeation rate ($\mu g/cm^2/min$) | Drops per hour of solvent through a glove (eye-drop size) | Permeation rate[A] |
|---|---|---|
| >9000 | 5001 or more | Not recommended (NR) |
| <9000 | 501 to 5000 | Poor (P) |
| <900 | | Fair (F) |
| <90 | 51 to 500 | Good (G) |
| <9 | 6 to 50 | Very good (VG) |
| <0.9 | 1 to 5 | Excellent |
| < detection level for 6hours | 0 to 0.5 | None detected (ND) |

**Table 11.5** Variations in glove permeation rates with temperature

| Glove Material | Chemical | | | | | |
|---|---|---|---|---|---|---|
| | Acetone | | | Ethyl acetate | | |
| | Breakthrough time (min) | | | | | |
| | 23°C/23°C | 23/35°C | 35/35°C | 23°C/23°C | 23/35°C | 35/35°C |
| Butyl | > 210 | > 210 | > 210 | > 210 | > 210 | > 210 |
| Nitrile | 4 | 7 | 6 | 30 | 22 | 14 |

## Penetration

Penetration is the bulk flow of chemicals and biological agents through closures, seams, porous areas, pinholes and other imperfections present in the glove. The extent of penetration, for certification purposes, is assessed on batches of gloves using hole detection methods. This procedure still allows a small but a significant proportion of the product to be sold with holes in it. This issue is of particular significance where protection is needed against dangerous pathogens and highly toxic or dangerous chemicals such as hydrofluoric acid. Where toxic, very toxic or corrosive substances are involved, employers should seek further assurance from the glove supplier and seek assurance that the product is suitable for the intended application. Alternatively, employers may set up their own glove leak test station and test each glove before use. A typical set up is described in EN 374 part 2.

Damaged gloves should not be used at any time, but it is not always practicable to detect the damage because a pinhole leak may not show visible signs of damage. One simple way of checking the integrity of the physical barrier is to hold the glove by the open (cuff) end and stretch this end so that the edges come close together forming a seal. Then roll up the closed cuff a few turns to reach near the wrist part of the glove. This action should inflate the fingers/palm areas of the glove (Figure 11.3). If there are any leaks, a hissing sound can be heard; alternatively the inflated glove can be immersed in a bucket of water to observe for air bubbles.

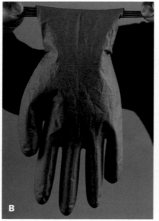

**Figure 11.3**

A series of photographs showing a simple method for detecting fine holes in a glove.

In **A**, the edge of the glove is stretched with small amount of air trapped inside the glove.

In **B**, the stretched glove is folded several times to squeeze the air into a smaller volume.

In **C**, further folding caused the air into a much smaller volume causing the expansion of the working area of the glove. If there are no holes one would see a 'pumped-up' glove like the one in C.

## Wicking

Coated gloves (fully or partly) are made with cotton or other suitable inner lining. In this case, the glove is manufactured by dip coating of the lining with the material of choice, such as poly vinyl chloride polymer (PVC), natural latex rubber, butyl rubber and so on. When the glove is manufactured by dip coating, strands of fibres, present in the lining, may protrude through the coating material. These fibres should be eliminated during the final production phase, but this may not happen on every occasion. A protruding fibre can act as a wick and will soak up chemicals through to the inner lining in contact with the skin. When purchasing lined gloves, always seek assurance from the supplier that wicking is not going to be a problem.

## Degradation

This is an alteration in the mechanical or physical properties of the glove material due to exposure to a chemical. This includes softening, swelling, shrinking, stiffening or simply dissolving in a chemical. Any of these effects can render the glove useless. The effects of rapid degradation are illustrated in Figure 11.4.

A glove that has been attacked by chemicals may become tacky, brittle or stiff. At present, there are no harmonised EN (European Norm) Standards for assessing degradation. Manufactures are at liberty to choose any test method they feel appropriate, but they are required to provide information on the resistance to degradation of their gloves by specific chemicals. Buyers should seek assurance from the supplier.

## Mechanical and physical factors

During use, glove material can be stretched, flexed, abraded, punctured, cut or torn. These will affect the physical barrier of the gloves. Therefore, the selection procedure should take account of the potential for glove damage by chemicals, mechanical forces and physical agents, such as cold.

## Glove Material

A variety of materials is used for the manufacture of chemical protective gloves. Each material (or combination of materials) has built-in advantages and disadvantages. Table 11.6 lists materials used in the manufacture of commonly available chemical protective gloves and their general performance characteristics. This information is useful for the selection of suitable gloves.

### Single-use Vs. Reusable Gloves

Reusable gloves are thick and generally 0.4mm to 0.8mm thick. They offer greater resistance to chemical permeation, abrasion, tear and puncture, and relatively longer breakthrough times than single-use gloves of the same material.

CE certified chemical protective gloves are tested for permeation breakthrough times and the maximum test period is 8 hours. This means that a glove may be reused several times within the permitted permeation time, but not beyond because there is a real potential that the wearer may be exposed to harm. An employer wanting to use a glove beyond the certified permeation breakthrough times should seek assurance from the supplier that the glove will remain effective for a prescribed length of time. The section on "permeation" provides practical advice on this matter.

Single-use gloves are thin, generally 0.01mm to 0.2mm thick. Although they are designed to provide good touch sensitivity and dexterity, many of them exhibit poor chemical resistance and breakthrough times. These gloves are useful for splash protection against chemicals. If used for this purpose, gloves should be changed soon after any splash contact or within the permitted permeation breakthrough time, after allowing a safety factor. Single-use gloves are designed for single use only and should be disposed after removing. It is almost impossible to put them on again without contaminating the skin and insides of the gloves.

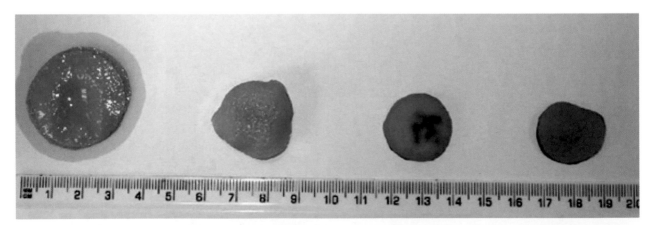

**Figure 11.4** Deterioration of reusable nitrile glove material due to solvent attack. The material has swollen several folds from its original size on the far right. Far left shows the material saturated with the solvent. This example illustrates the importance of correct selection.

**Table 11.6** Glove materials advantages and disadvantages

| Glove material | Advantages and disadvantages |
|---|---|
| Natural rubber -latex | • Good for water miscible substances, weak acids and alkalis (pH range 4 to 10)<br>• Good for biohazards, ensure no pinholes<br>• Poor for organic solvents, oils and grease<br>Single-use gloves, in particular, may cause latex protein allergy (respiratory and skin). The need to use single-use latex gloves will require justification by risk assessment. Where justified use powder-free, low protein types |
| Nitrile | • Good for water miscible substances, weak acids and alkalis (pH range 4 to 10)<br>• Good for aliphatic solvents, oils and grease<br>• Good for biohazards, ensure no pinholes<br>• Poor for direct contact with ketones<br>• Good for splash protection |
| Poly vinyl choloride (PVC) | • Good for water miscible substances, weak acids and alkali solutions (pH range 4 to 10)<br>• Poor for organic solvents |
| Butyl rubber | • Good for water miscible substances<br>• Good for strong acids (pH range 1 to 3)<br>• Good for ketones and esters<br>• Poor for solvents, in general |
| Neoprene | • Good for water miscible substances<br>• Good for strong alkalis (pH range 11 to 14), phenols<br>• Poor for organic solvents |
| Viton (PTFE) | • Good for chlorinated hydrocarbons, aromatic and aliphatic solvents, and PCBs<br>• Poor for ketones<br>• Very expensive<br>• Poor touch sensitivity |
| Poly vinyl alcohol (PVA) | • Good for organic solvents<br>• No good in the presence of water |

## Workplace Factors

Many workplace factors can influence the extent of protection provided by a glove, some of which are discussed below.

## Task Factors

The glove selected should not present serious impediment to the performance of the task, but it should provide adequate protection against chemicals and the task related factors. It should provide sufficient dexterity, grip and comfort and at the same time should be able to withstand the rigours of the tasks (i.e. the way in which the task involving a chemical is undertaken).

## Dexterity

Thicker glove materials offer greater resistance to chemical permeation and mechanical damage. However, a thick glove can impair grip and dexterity. Loss of grip or touch sensitivity can compromise wearer safety, reduce productivity and comfort. For these reasons alone employers need to be sure that the hands do not come into contact with chemicals and adequate SWD is established in other ways.

## Cuff length

The cuff length should be long enough to prevent ingress of chemicals and water. Most single-use gloves are manufactured with short cuff lengths, long enough to cover a small part of the forearm and this fact should be taken into account during selection.

### Grip

For most jobs, grip is essential to ensure safe handling and accident prevention. To improve grip, glove surfaces can be made roughened or textured. These properties are available in different grades. However, for certain jobs (e.g. shampooing hair) a roughened glove surface is not acceptable. All-round smooth gloves are available for activities where snagging should be avoided.

### Resistance to Abrasion, Puncture, Cut and Tear

Glove selection procedure should take account of these elements and the right grades should be selected. A clear analysis of the ways in which the task is to be carried out will provide relevant information.

### Incidental Contact and Intentional Contact

Incidental contact refers to tasks: where there is no intended direct contact with **hazardous substances**; the task has been designed with adequate SWD; and any skin exposure will only occur through accidental spill or splash.

Intentional contact refers to tasks where skin comes into contact with chemicals by immersion and direct handling or direct contact. When hands are immersed in chemicals or water to accomplish tasks, employers should be sure that they have considered alternative approaches for prevention or adequate control of the exposure. Where it is not reasonably practicable to avoid immersion of the hands, this fact should be recorded with reasons. The same applies to situations where direct contact (e.g. direct handling of solvent soaked rag) is allowed. However, there are situations where prevention or adequate control by means other than PPE is not reasonably practicable. For example, when hairdressers are shampooing and colouring clients' hair. In such cases, gloves are relied upon for adequate SWD.

### Internal Contamination of Glove

Internal contamination of gloves brings chemicals, water and **micro-organisms** into intimate contact with the skin and aids prolonged contact. It may happen due to various incorrect use patterns. Examples include:

- Incorrect donning and doffing of gloves;
- Using glove inside-out with a view to prolong the use of the glove (Figure 11.5).
- Seepage of chemicals around the edges of the glove. For example, due to inadequate cuff length (Figure 8.16) or incorrect work practice (Figure 11.6a);
- Using damaged gloves. This can allow rapid penetration and permeation of hazardous substances;
- Incorrect storage in the workplace (Figure 11.6b);

**Figure 11.5** This glove had been used incorrectly.

It was turned inside out to extend the usage life (glove user's opinion and action). The action led to the contamination of hands, skin exposure and dermal uptake.

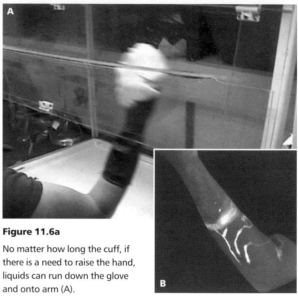

**Figure 11.6a**

No matter how long the cuff, if there is a need to raise the hand, liquids can run down the glove and onto arm (A).

This effect (B) was demonstrated with the help of fluorescent tracer mixed in the cleaning agent. First priority should be to look for alternative ways to accomplish the task. Where small amount of run-off is expected, a part of the cuff could be folded-back to act as a drip catcher.

**Figure 11.6b** Incorrect storage of a glove.

In this case, one glove is left in the solvent trough and a contaminated lid is placed on top. The work surfaces are heavily contaminated indicating a lack of good house keeping.

This situation presents considerable potential for dermal exposure by many pathways. The spatula with the red paint was used with suitable safe working distance to maintain product quality and to minimise product rejection.

This practice has a positive contribution to minimise skin contact, but a similar approach is absent during cleaning tasks and house keeping.

## Environment Factors

### Temperature and Humidity

Extreme cold and hot conditions can affect the structure and integrity of some glove material. In these circumstances, gloves can become brittle and cracks may appear. This situation can affect the protective performance of gloves. High temperature conditions can significantly reduce the permeation breakthrough times and may cause degradation of the glove material. Some glove materials can be affected by high humidity or water. For example, poly vinyl alcohol (PVA) gloves cannot be used in the presence of water because the glove will simply dissolve in it.

### Wearer Factors

Inherent in the use of any glove are the drawbacks associated with sweating, occlusion and loss of dexterity, sensitivity, flexibility and movement of fingers. These can cause:

- Wearer discomfort;
- Simple tasks taking a longer time to complete or made completely impractical;
- Potential loss of grip and touch;
- Temptation to remove or not to use gloves.

In order to achieve the maximum protective performance from a glove, it is essential to match the glove to the wearer and involve them in the selection procedure.

### Size

Wearing an incorrectly sized glove can cause accidents and this can happen in many ways. For example:

- Loss of grip and dexterity;
- Folds in the glove leading to trapping and snagging;
- Oversized glove leading to trapping.
- If the glove is too small or too large for the hand, the wearer may feel uncomfortable and this can result in a variety of behavioural patterns.

- A very close fitting glove can cause significant occlusion and may also cause muscular fatigue.

However, there is always a trade-off between comfort and protection. It is easy to select the right size as shown in Figure 11.7. Employers should make available a range of sizes to suit their workforce. Table 11.7 shows the relationship between hands and glove sizes.

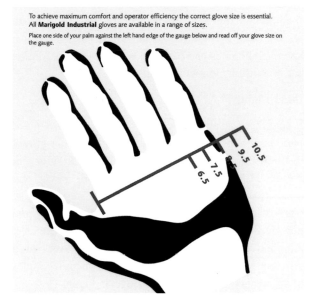

To achieve maximum comfort and operator efficiency the correct glove size is essential. All **Marigold Industrial** gloves are available in a range of sizes.

Place one side of your palm against the left hand edge of the gauge below and read off your glove size on the gauge.

**Figure 11.7** An example of a glove size selection chart. Users can identify the correct size by placing their hand as instructed. *Photograph: Courtesy of Marigold Industrial Ltd., Hambrook, Bristol, England, UK.*

### Skin irritation and Sensitisation

Skin needs to "breathe". Chemical protective glove materials, by design, are "impervious" to water. Because of this, sweat from the skin may accumulate in the space between the skin and the glove inner surface. If the accumulation of water or sweat is allowed to continue for prolonged periods, the skin may become damaged due to irritation caused by chemicals in the sweat. If the glove is not aired adequately during storage, unhealthy micro-organisms may grow on the inner surfaces of the glove, which, in turn, can affect the skin.

**Table 11.7** Glove and hand sizes

| Hand size | Hand circumference (mm) | Hand length (mm) | Glove size | Minimum total length of glove (mm) |
|---|---|---|---|---|
| 6 | 152 | 160 | 6 | 220 |
| 7 | 178 | 171 | 7 | 230 |
| 8 | 203 | 182 | 8 | 240 |
| 9 | 229 | 192 | 9 | 250 |
| 10 | 254 | 204 | 10 | 260 |
| 11 | 279 | 215 | 11 | 270 |

## Glove Breaks

Wearers should be able to take 'glove-breaks' in order that the skin can breathe normally and recover. The frequency of glove breaks needs to be decided on a case by case basis. For example, hairdressers use single-use, unlined disposable vinyl gloves for shampooing hair. In this situation, a one or two minute glove-break can be taken immediately after shampooing a client and before shampooing the next client. During the glove-break period, other preparatory work can be carried out. An approach like this can be fitted within the work routine and without any loss of productivity.

## Inner Lining

Where chemical protective gloves are worn for prolonged periods, it is practicable to wear separate inner gloves made of fine absorbent material such as cotton or silk Figure 11.8a. They should help absorb sweat and minimise sweat-related skin irritation and improve comfort. Inner gloves should be cleaned regularly and prevented from becoming contaminated with chemicals. Alternatively, suitably lined dip-coated gloves or a different type of technology could be applied. Examples of different types of gloves are shown in Figure 11.8b.

## Glove Related Skin Problems

Materials used in the manufacture of a glove may cause skin irritation or allergy. There are many examples of this. Natural rubber proteins may leach out from single-use latex gloves and can cause skin irritation and allergic reactions. Where it is not reasonably practicable to avoid using single-use latex gloves, powder-free, low protein gloves should be selected.

Plasticisers and preservatives are essential components of all types of synthetic gloves. Many of these chemicals can cause irritation or allergy to the skin, if they are released from the gloves and come into contact with the skin. Reputable manufacturers have designed their glove curing processes to minimise these effects.

## SELECTING AND USING SUITABLE GLOVES

There is a huge variety of chemical protective gloves on the market. These vary in design, materials used and the way in which they are fabricated. There is a good chance that a glove can be found to suit almost every application, but finding that right glove requires considerable care, expertise and attention to detail.

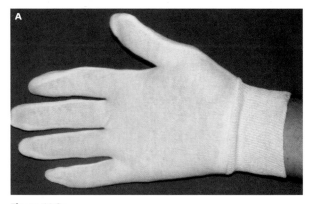
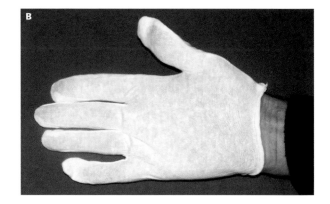

**Figure 11.8a**

**A** shows a fine cotton inner glove.  **B** shows a fine silk glove.

These can be worn inside chemical protective gloves to help increase comfort and absorb excess sweat. Inner gloves should be kept clean by ensuring correct donning and doffing of chemical protective gloves. These gloves can be laundered in accordance with the manufacturer's instructions.

**Figure 11.8b**

Technological improvements have enabled glove manufactures to incorporate improved grip to hold slippery objects; to absorb moisture in sweat; to use multi layer coatings with different materials to improve flexibility, comfort, durability and chemical protection.

Photographs A, B and C show examples of gloves incorporating these features. *Photographs A and B: Courtesy of Ansell Healthcare Europe N.V, Brussels, Belgium. Photograph C: Courtesy of Marigold Industrial Ltd., Hambrook, Bristol, England, UK.*

## Glove Selector

There are many approaches to the selection of adequate and suitable gloves. A simple step-by-step approach is proposed in this book and is shown in the glove selector (Figure 11.9). The answers to the questions should provide sufficient information to the manufacturer or supplier of gloves to be able to recommend suitable options to meet the requirements. The selection procedure should always fully involve the wearers. It will:

- Help them to understand the subtle issues that influence the selection and use of gloves;

- Maximise the acceptance of the selected gloves; and

- Ensure that the gloves are used correctly where and when needed.

## Filling Out the Glove Selector

### Step 1: Administrative Information

Fill in the basic administrative details about the *company, department, section, task* details for which gloves are needed, the *name of the person* completing the glove selector and the *date* completed.

### Step 2: Control Information

#### Control Measures

The control measures box should list the *control measures* (other than PPE) that are in use for adequate control of dermal exposure taking account of the dermal exposure pathways (see Chapter 6) relevant to the task. It should describe what measures are in place for achieving adequate SWD. Implementing adequate SWD is an essential part of the requirement for adequate control and should minimise the need for gloves.

#### Reason for using gloves

Tick the appropriate reasons for wanting to use gloves. Use the following definitions. *Residual risk:* There is still a skin exposure risk after all other reasonable control measures have been put in place. These measures should be listed in the 'control measures' and 'SWD' sections; *Short duration work:* Other control measures are not reasonably practicable to avoid hands coming into contact with chemicals or wet-work. For example, an infrequent task that takes less than an hour to complete or a short-term task that is carried out infrequently at different locations; *Interim measure:* Gloves are needed while designing and/or installing other control measures for avoiding contacts with hands; *Temporary failure:* Dermal exposure control measures in place have broken down. Gloves are needed while fixing the control measures; *Emergency work/rescue:* Emergency work that can not wait until other dermal exposure control

measures can be put in place. It means, an emergency situation has risen and gloves are needed to deal with the situation. Alternatively, gloves are needed for emergency rescue; *Controls at source - not reasonably practical:* Due to the nature of the work, there aren't any reasonably practicable measures for application at source. A typical example is shampooing clients' hair; *In case of control measures failure:* It is considered to be prudent to issue PPE, not because other control measures are inadequate on their own, but to provide protection in case those control measures fail to operate.

### Step 3: Product Information

#### Substances used in the task

To complete this section correctly prepared safety data sheets (SDS) are needed. For those substances and products bought-in contact the suppliers. They have a legal duty to supply SDS in compliance with the law. In some case you may have to write to the supplier to seek clarification about the substances (e.g. the SDS says "petroleum based solvents") or control measures advice. Where this is necessary, a sample letter in Chapter 7 may be used. If the substances used in the task are manufactured at the site, then the employer has the responsibility to generate SDS. For process generated substances, list what is being generated. You should know this information from experience, otherwise your trade association may be able to help. If you are unable to complete the details, seek specialist help (e.g. occupational hygienists). Where wet-work is involved, indicate this information as well as the substances involved in the wet-work.

#### Amount used

*Small:* Grams or millilitres (a few ounces, around a cupful) of substance; *Medium:* Kilograms or litres (1-100 kg, up to 55 gallon drums); *Large:* Tonnes or cubic metres (tanker or lorry loads).

#### Physical forms encountered during the task

For s*olids*, indicate dustiness as low, medium or large following the guide and use the code to fill the selector. For example, dustiness low would be indicated by DL. *Dustiness – Low (DL):* Pellets, waxy flakes and pill-like solids that do not break up easily. No dust cloud produced and little or no dust in the surrounding areas and work surfaces; *Dustiness – Medium (DM):* Crystalline granular solids and dust (visible, settles quickly). Fumes or mist formed close to the task but dissipates very quickly; *Dustiness – High (DH):* Fine powder, fume or mist. Dust cloud, fume or mist is formed and remains in the air for several minutes. **Liquid** – *Free flowing (LF)* means like water; *Liquid – Viscous (LV)* means the substance/product sticks to the surfaces like phenol.

**Figure 11.9** Information for selecting chemical protective gloves

| STEP 1: Administrative Information | |
|---|---|
| Company | Department |
| Completed by | Section |
| Task details | |
| Task Location | Date Prepared |

| STEP 2: Control Information | |
|---|---|
| Control Measures (in place) | Reason for using gloves |
| | Residual risk |
| | Short duration work |
| | Interim measure |
| Safe Working Distance Measures | Temporary failure |
| | Emergency work |
| | Controls at source – not reasonably practical |
| | In case of control measures failure |

**STEP 3: Substances/Product Information**

| Substances (used in the task) | Amount used<br>Small    Medium    Large<br>(g or ml)    (kg or l)    (Tonnes) | Forms encountered during the task<br>(Solids - low dust, medium dust, high dust;<br>Liquid - free flowing, viscous) |
|---|---|---|
| 1 | | |
| 2 | | |
| 3 | | |

Liquid Medium

Water-based        Solvent based        oil based        other: water/solvent mix; water/oil mix

**STEP 4: Work Related Information**

| | |
|---|---|
| Task duration (minutes) | Task frequency/day |

Dermal exposure pathways

Immersion      Direct contact      Splashes      Surface contact      Deposition

| | |
|---|---|
| Dexterity requirement<br>Low    Medium    High | Grip requirements<br>Low      High |
| Abrasion potential<br>Low      High | Cut potential<br>Low      High |
| Tear potential<br>Low      High | Puncture potential<br>Low      High |
| Humidity in the area where gloves are used<br>Dry    Wet | Temperature at which gloves are to be used<br>(°C) |

**STEP 5: Wearers Related Information**

| | |
|---|---|
| Likely exposure areas<br><br>Hands    Wrists    Forearms | Glove exposure pattern<br>Intermittent use      Change after each use<br><br>Regular use |
| Glove sizes required<br>6   7   8   9   10   11 | Inner liner required (to absorb excess sweat)<br>Yes      No |

Types of inner liner required:

**Any Other Relevant Information** (e.g. hot spatter may land on the skin; paper work during the task; pH)

Seek individual wearer information: e.g. (i) Missing fingers; (ii) known allergies or skin conditions.

**Liquid medium**

For liquid based substance or product indicate whether it is *water based* (dissolved in water) and note the pH of the working solution; *solvent based* (pure solvent, dissolved in a solvent or dissolved in a mixture of solvents) or an *oil based* product. For example, diluted metal working fluid should be indicated as water/oil mix.

**Step 4: Work Related Information**

*Task duration* - provide information on how long it takes to do the work (task); *Task frequency* - indicate how many times this work is done each day.

**Dermal exposure pathways: *Immersion*:** Hands are immersed in chemicals to accomplish the task because there are no other alternative ways of doing the task; *Direct contact*: Hands come into direct contact with contaminated work pieces or items containing the substances listed in Step 2. It is not reasonably practical to establish SWD by means other than gloves; *Splashes*: Liquid splash or dust "splash" comes into contact with hands; *Surface contact*: Hands come into contact with contaminated work surfaces, clothing, work tools, footwear, etc. even after control measures at source have been put in place; *Deposition:* Hands come into contact with dust, fume and/or mist contaminants in air.

**Likely exposure areas: *Hands; wrists; forearms*** – tick as appropriate

**Dexterity requirement**: *Low* - size of the work piece handled is greater than 10mm in length or diameter; *Medium* - size of the work piece handled is greater than 5mm and less than 10mm in length or diameter; *High* - size of the work piece handled is less than 5mm in length or diameter.

**Grip requirements**: *Low* - the extent of grip is not critical for the task carried out, for the glove wearer and/or the safe system of work; *High* - the extent of grip is critical for the task carried out, for the glove wearer and/or the safe system of work.

**Tear potential**: *Low* - it is <u>unlikely</u> that the task carried out, work pieces used /handled and the areas surrounding the task would cause a tear to a typical rubber glove used for household cleaning; *High* - it is likely that the task carried out, work pieces used/handled and the areas surrounding would cause a tear to a rubber glove.

**Abrasion potential**: *Low* - handling procedures (including rotational, pulling and pushing movements) used for performing the task <u>do not act</u> like sand paper to cause abrasion to unprotected skin. *High* - handling procedures (including rotational, pulling and pushing movements) used for performing the task would act like sand paper to cause abrasion to unprotected skin.

**Puncture potential**: *Low* - the way in which the task is carried out is <u>unlikely</u> to cause damage or injury to hands by sharp or irregularly shaped objects and sharp tools. *High* - the way in which the task is carried out is <u>likely</u> to cause damage or injury to the hands by sharp or irregularly shaped objects and sharp tools.

**Cut potential**: *Low* - the way in which the task is carried out is <u>unlikely</u> to cause cuts to the skin. *High* - the way in which the task is carried out is <u>likely</u> to cause cuts to the skin.

**Humidity in the area where gloves are used**: *Dry* - the area in which glove is to be used is like an office environment or a typical engineering workshop. *Wet* - the area in which the glove is to be used is visibly wet or steamed up like a shower room in use.

**Temperature at which gloves are to be used (ºC)**: Indicate the maximum and minimum temperature that would be faced by the glove surface when performing the task.

**Step 5: Wearer Related Factors**

**Likely exposed areas:** Indicate the areas of the hands to be exposed to substances listed in step 3.

**Glove use pattern**: *Intermittent* - the need to use gloves is irregular throughout the day. *Change after each use* - glove should be changed soon after the task is completed and not reused. *Regular* - gloves are used throughout the day and almost continuously, except for breaks.

**Glove sizes required:** Identify the people who will need to wear gloves for the task and indicate the sizes required to suit the wearers.

**Inner gloves required**: Indicate yes or no. If it is practicable to use fine inner gloves, they will help to absorb sweat and make it more comfortable to wear the protective gloves.

**Types of inner gloves required**: Some protective gloves are made with inner cotton or synthetic liners. Indicate inner lined gloves, cotton, silk or synthetic type inner glove. Consult users for preference.

**Any other relevant information**: Suppliers of gloves will base their recommendations on the answers listed in the glove selector. In this box, provide any other information likely to be useful for suitable glove selection. Having used the glove selector to identify the general types and sizes to suit the work and the workforce involved, in this section, consider any particular needs of individual wearers. Examples are given in the selector.

**Using Chemical Protective Gloves**

The law demands that PPE including gloves is the last line of protection. Where it is necessary to use gloves, their use should be integrated within normal work activities. To achieve this, the users should be instructed on where and when gloves should be worn and they should be trained to correctly put them on and take them off. Correct donning and doffing procedures for reusable and single-use gloves are shown in Figure 11.10.

Gloves should be free of internal contamination and used within their capability (e.g. permeation breakthrough time, degradation, puncture resistance). Reusable gloves should be stored in environments where cross contamination or exposure to chemicals can be prevented. Correct storage is also important for the airing of the inner surfaces of gloves.

It is good practice to designate and signpost the areas where PPE is needed. The people affected by this procedure should know the reasons why the area has been designated as such and the benefits of such designation.

## CHEMICAL PROTECTIVE CLOTHING

### What is it?

Chemical protective clothing (CPC) may be defined as clothing which is designed and certified for the protection of the body against chemical solids, liquids, vapours

and/or gases. Table 11.8 describes the EN classification of CPC. It should be noted that conformation to these standards and a 'CE' mark does not mean that every type of CPC is 100% impervious to the hazard for which it is designed. Under the CE certification scheme, a CPC is only required to meet the minimum performance requirements. For example, in the case of Type 5 CPC, the suits are allowed inward leakage of up to 30% (for individual suits during test), providing an average for the series of suits tested is less than 15%.

The design requirements and the EN certification procedures for CPC mean they are not certified for use for protection against micro-organisms and radioactive particulate hazards. Protective clothing for these hazards will require different approaches to design, testing and certification. To claim protection against radioactive particulates and micro-organisms, a CPC should be subjected to additional tests specified in relevant EN Standards. CPC can be a combination of specified individual items put together or may be a single piece of protective clothing. Figure 11.11 shows typical design characteristics used in Type 2 CPC. Figure 11.12 shows examples of two types of CPC. Each type has its own features and has been designed to deliver protection against chemicals specified by the manufacturer.

### Correct removal of gloves
Reusable gloves (chemically resistant)

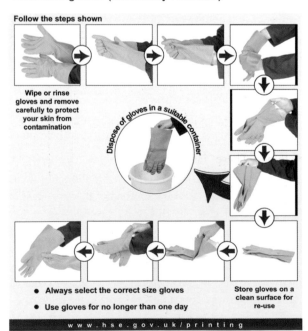

### Correct removal of gloves
Single use gloves (splash resistant)

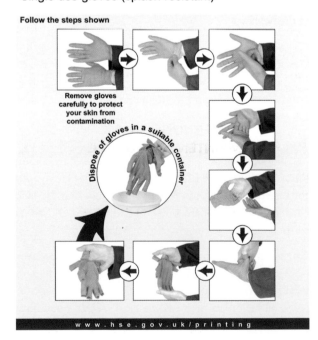

**Figure 11.10**

**A** is a poster illustrating the correct removal and wearing of reusable gloves.
**B** is a poster illustrating the correct removal of single-use gloves.
*Both posters are available free for download from the Health and Safety Executive's (HSE) 'Skin at Work' website.*

**Table 11.8** EN Standards for CPC design, performance testing and certification

| Pictogram | EN Type | EN Standard | Description |
|---|---|---|---|
| | Type 1 | EN 943 - 1<br>EN 943 - 2 | **Gas Tight Protective Clothing**<br>Protective clothing against liquid and gaseous chemicals, aerosols and solid particulates |
| | Type 2 | EN 943 - 1 | **Non Gas Tight Protective Clothing**<br>Suits prevent ingress of dusts, liquids and vapours |
| | Type 3 | EN 14605 | **Liquid Tight Suits**<br>Suits which can protect against strong and directional jets of liquid chemical |
| | Type 4 | EN 14605 | **Spray Tight Suits**<br>Suits which offer protection against saturation of liquid chemicals |
| | Type 5 | EN 13982 – 1 and 2 | **Dry Particles Suits**<br>Suits which provide protection to the full body against airborne solid particulates |
| | Type 6 | En 13034 | **Reduced Spray Suit**<br>Suits which offer limited protection against a light spray of liquid chemicals |

**Note:** EN approved CPC should carry the chemical pictogram shown (flask and vapour). EN standards do not demand the use of other pictograms (Type 2 to Type 6) to pictorially illustrate the information shown in the "Description" column. It is a weakness of EN Standards. However, manufacturers use these pictograms to help users. *Pictograms: Courtesy of the DuPont Engineering Products s.a.r.l, L-2984, Luxembourg.*

## SELECTION, USE AND MAINTENANCE OF CPC

Table 11.9 provides a guide on where a particular type of CPC may be used. The classification is based on the recommendations of the British Standard Institution (BSI). This guide is based on COSHH Essentials (CE) health hazard groups (see Chapter 9) and hazard classification under the CHIP regulations (see Chapter 7). The classification is further explained by potential scenarios where a particular type of CPC may be useful. However, the principles for the selection and use of adequate and suitable CPC are similar to the selection of gloves for chemical protection. Essentially, all the factors described for the selection of gloves, (see Figure 11.9), will apply equally to the selection of adequate and

suitable CPC. In addition, selection of CPC should take detailed account of the nature of chemical challenge to the clothing. These include the physical state of the chemical(s) and how they may present themselves to the wearer - gas/vapour cloud; fume; mist; spray; jet; splash; bulk liquid; airborne or surface settled particulates.

Although a CE marked CPC may be tested for resistance to permeation against a battery of chemicals, the selection process should ensure that the CPC selected is adequate and suitable for the chosen purpose.

Reusable CPC should be cleaned, maintained and stored strictly in accordance with the manufacturer's instruction. Any failure to do so may compromise the health and safety of wearers.

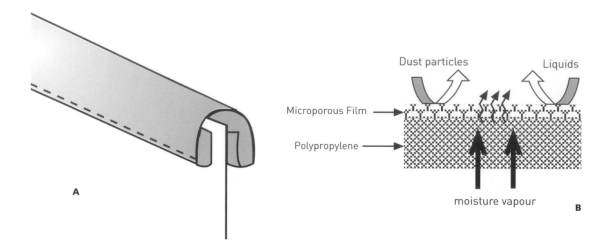

**Figure 11.11**

The design requirements of European and other Standards help to ensure that liquid droplets/sprays and dust particles do not go through the fabric and seams. This figure shows typical design characteristics used in spray tight chemical protective clothing (CPC).

**A** illustrates an approach for the construction of seams. This type of construction will greatly minimise contaminants passing through the seams.

**B** illustrates the typical manufacturing/design characteristics, of spray and dry particulate tight CPC fabrics, to prevent contaminants passing through the fabric but enables sweat (moisture) to escape through the material to improve wearer comfort.

*Photograph: Courtesy of Microgard Ltd., Kingston upon Hull, England, UK.*

**Figure 11.12**

Picture **A** shows an example seamless chemical protective clothing (CPC) for protection against sprays and dry particulates (e.g. isocyanate containing paint aerosols). **B** shows an example of a CPC for protection against liquids, solvent jets and dry particulates (e.g. acids).

*Photograph A: Courtesy of DuPont Engineering Products s.a.r.l, L-2984, Luxembourg.  Photograph B: Microgard Ltd., Kingston upon Hull, England, UK.*

**Table 11.9** An approach for the selection of CPC

| CPC Type | Description | Hazard Class and Physical Form | COSHH Essentials Health Hazard Group A | Example Application | Usability |
|---|---|---|---|---|---|
| 1a | Gas tight suit worn with breathing apparatus (BA) inside | Very Toxic; Gaseous phase | D and E | Fumigation | Reusable and limited use (R&L) |
| 1b | Gas tight suit with BA outside | Very Toxic; Gaseous phase | D and E | Large volumes of volatile liquids | R&L |
| 1c | Gas tight suit with airline BA | Very Toxic; Gaseous phase | D and E | Large volumes of volatile liquids | R&L |
| 1ET | Gas tight suit for emergency teams | Very Toxic; Gaseous phase | D and E | Emergency teams | R&L |
| 2 | Non-gas tight suit with air line BA | Very Toxic; Mist/aerosols of non-volatile liquids | D and E | Pharmaceutical production | R&L |
| 3 | Liquid tight suit | Very Toxic; Unbroken jet of non-volatile liquids | D and E | Acids under pressure in pipelines | R&L |
| 3ET | Liquid tight suit for emergency teams | Very Toxic; Unbroken jet of non-volatile liquids | D and E | Emergency teams | R&L |
| 4 | Spray tight suit | Toxic/Harmful; Spray of non-volatile liquid | C and B | Spray paint application | R&L |
| 5 | Particle protective garment | Toxic/Harmful; Solids including asbestos and lead | C and B | Asbestos removal | R&L |
| 6 | Limited protection garment | Irritants and skin; Spray drift | A | Spraying low toxicity pesticides | R&L |

Note: A – see Chapter 9 for more detail

## CONCLUSION

The essential lesson is that PPE does not become adequate and suitable just because it is carrying the chemical protection pictogram, a reference to a Standard (ISO/CEN/BSI/ASTM), a marking of the certification body and a 'CE' marking or similar. PPE carries all these signs for the simple reason that it has satisfied the relevant requirements in a laboratory test. As explained earlier, the selection and use of adequate and suitable PPE is the responsibility of the employer. The step-by-step glove selection procedure, described in this Chapter, can be used for this purpose. A similar approach can be applied for the selection of adequate and suitable CPC.

Incorrect selection, use or maintenance of PPE can compromise the health and safety of wearers. Maximum benefits can be achieved when the users of PPE are closely involved in the selection of PPE. The essential elements for benefits realisation are explained in Chapter 14.

## TEST YOUR KNOWLEDGE

1. Explain why PPE carrying the CE marking and a reference to a Standard to which it is manufactured will not automatically meet the requirements of being adequate and suitable.

2. In law, PPE is considered as the last resort for protection. Explain why.

3. There are situations where PPE may be used as the last resort. Describe the conditions that will meet this requirement and relate them to a situation found in your workplace.

4. List and explain five examples that should be taken into account when selecting suitable gloves.

5. Explain your approach to the selection of suitable PPE for a high pressure spray application of antifouling paint (tributyl tin oxide dispersed in toluene, butyl-acetate and trimethylbenzene) to the outer bottom of a large container ship docked in an enclosed dry dock. The work takes place on a very warm Summer's day.

## FURTHER READING

**A novel method of assessing the effectiveness of protective gloves.** KS Creely, JW Cherrie. Annals of Occupational Hygiene; 45 (2001):137-143.

**Approximation of Personal Protective Equipment Laws Directive** (89/686/EEC) as amended by Directives 93/68/EEC, 93/95/EEC and 96/58/EEC. Official Journal of the European Communities, No. L 399/18, 30.12.89.

**Cost effectiveness of chemical protective gloves for the workplace (HSG206).** HSE Books, Sudbury, UK. ISBN 0 7176 1828 5.

**Critique of assumptions about selecting chemical-resistant gloves: A case for workplace evaluation of glove efficacy.** TD Klinger and MF Boeniger. Applied Occupational and Environmental Hygiene; 17 (2002): 360-367.

Dermal absorption of chlorpyrifos. DT Mage. Annals of Occupational Hygiene; 50 (2006): 638 – 639.

**Dermal uptake of solvent from the vapour phase: an experimental study in humans.** I Brooke, J Cocker, JI Delic et al. Annals of Occupational Hygiene; 42 (1998): 531- 540.

**Formaldehyde in reusable protective gloves.** A Ponten. Contact Dermatitis; 54(2006): 268-271.

**Gloves as chemical protection – Can they really work.** C Packham. Annals of Occupational Hygiene; 50 (2006): 545-548.

**Helping Hands.** N Vaughan. Health and Safety International; (2004): 1 –5.

**In-use testing and interpretation of chemical resistant gloves performance.** M Boeniger, T Klingner. Applied Occupational and Environmental Hygiene; 17 (2002): 368-378.

**Internal contamination of gloves: Routes and consequences.** BV Rawson, J Cocker, PG Evans, JP Wheeler and PM Akrill. Annals of Occupational Hygiene; 49 (2005): 535-541.

**Knowledge of skin hazards and the use of gloves by Australian hairdressing students and practising hairdressers.** R Nixon, H Roberts, K Frowen, M Sim. Contact dermatitis; 54 (2006): 112-116.

**Let's dispel a few myths.** Bad Hand Days. www.badhandday.hse.gov.uk

**Main non-conformities of protective clothing detected in the Spanish market.** I Caceres, J Bahima, E Cohen,. Centro Nacional de Medios de Protection (INSHT). www.mtas.es/insht/en/research

**Modelling the temperature dependence of N-methylpyrrilinone permeation through butyl- and natural-rubber gloves.** Zeller ET, Sulewski R. American Industrial Hygiene Association Journal; 54 (1993): 465-479.

**Occupational allergic contact dermatitis from bisphenol A in vinyl gloves.** L Matthieu, AFL Godoi, J Lambert, RV Grieken. Contact Dermatitis; 49(2004) 281-283.

**Personal protective equipment and dermal exposure.** PG Evans, JJ McAlinden, P Griffin. Applied Occupational and Environmental Hygiene; 16 (2001): 334-337.

**Potential exposure of hands inside protective gloves – a summary of data from non-agricultural pesticide surveys.** ANI Garrod, AM Phillips, JA Pemberton. Annals of Occupational Hygiene; 45 (2001): 55-60.

**Protective gloves against chemicals and micro-organisms.** British Standards Institution, London UK. EN 374 (parts 1, 2 and 3).

**Protective gloves – General requirements and test methods.** British Standards Institution, London UK. EN 420:2003.

**Protective gloves for occupational use.** A Boman, T Estlander, JE Wahlberg, HI Maibach. CRC Press. New York, USA. ISBN 0 8493 1558 1.

**Selection, use and maintenance of chemical protective clothing – Guidance.** British Standards Institution, London UK. BS7184:2001.

**Standard test method for resistance of protective materials to permeation by liquids and gases under continuous contact.** American Society for Testing and Materials. ASTM Method F739-99.

**Temperature as a variable in evaluating the permeability of 1,1,1-tricholroethane through four types of chemical protective clothing.** B Alexy, RM Buchan. American Industrial Hygiene Association Journal; 48 (1987): A104-A109.

**The effect of glove flexure on permeation parameters.** JL Perkins, KC Rainey. Applied Occupational and Environmental Hygiene; 12 (1997); 206-210.

# Chapter 12

# Personal Hygiene and Skin Protection

## INTRODUCTION

Human skin is a complex organ and performs a variety of protective functions as explained in Chapter 2. Healthy, hydrated and undamaged skin is essential for maintaining its protective functions. To this end, a good standard of personal hygiene plays an important maintenance role because it helps to limit the damage to the barrier properties of the skin.

One of the key components of personal hygiene is the use of skin care products. Depending on their functions and properties, they can help to protect the barrier layer, remove dirt and excess water on the skin or help to restore oils and moisture lost from the skin. This Chapter describes the essential components of personal hygiene welfare facilities at work and the factors to be considered for the selection and use of skin care products. Skin care products fall within the second aspect (protect the skin) of the APC approach described in Chapter 9.

## ESSENTIAL COMPONENTS OF PERSONAL HYGIENE AT WORK

The law requires that employers should provide adequate welfare facilities to ensure that their employees can maintain a good standard of personal hygiene, which is needed for achieving adequate control of exposure to *hazardous agents* and *wet-work*. Essential components of adequate personal hygiene welfare facilities at work are listed below. Additional requirements may be stipulated by agent (e.g. lead, asbestos and biological agents) specific regulations.

- Changing facilities including separate storage facilities for clean and dirty clothing;
- Skin cleansing facilities including running hot and cold water. Portable or transportable welfare facilities including waterless cleaning/disinfection systems are available for use in transient sites;
- Facilities for drying the wet skin;

- Measures to reduce the spread of contaminants from the washing and changing facilities;
- Eating and drinking facilities including the provision of drinking water;
- Provision of pre-work creams, where necessary;
- Provision of skin conditioning creams, where necessary;
- Provision of sanitising products, where necessary.

**Changing Facilities**

Changing facilities should be provided when employees are required to wear protective clothing to prevent or minimise exposure to hazardous agents. The facilities provided should be designed and located to prevent contaminant transfer from the protective clothing onto street clothing, to other areas of the workplace, public transport systems and private homes. There have been cases where highly toxic substances, such as asbestos fibres and lead dust, were transferred from work to homes. In these situations, third parties including children may be put at risk. Contaminants on protective and street clothing may act as a "sink" from which ingestion, skin and inhalation exposures can take place.

When work is undertaken at transient sites, (e.g. construction work on a motorway, emergency roadside assistance for motor vehicles and repairs to sewerage systems), employers should ensure that suitable arrangements are in place for donning, doffing and storage of protective clothing, and employees involved are informed and instructed on correct use and storage.

Changing facilities provided should be maintained to promote good personal hygiene practices and the standard of maintenance should comply with relevant legislative requirements. The practice of using compressed air to remove dusts from coveralls and surfaces should not be tolerated. This practice can lead to significant inhalation exposure and the contaminants could be transferred from one area to another.

## Washing Facilities

Hand washing facilities should be provided and sited at readily accessible places. Showers should be provided where whole body decontamination is required. Hand washing facilities will include the provision of skin cleansers, hand drying facilities and skin care creams (pre and after work creams) where necessary.

## Eating and Drinking Facilities

A suitable uncontaminated area should be provided for consuming food and drinks. A suitable facility at a permanent site will include seating, tables, heating provision and an area for safe storage of food. It is also necessary to provide an adequate supply of drinking water. For transient sites, suitable arrangements should be set up on a case by case basis. For example, eating and drinking area in a vehicle used for emergency roadside assistance could be the driver's compartment segregated from the rest of the vehicle. At a semi-permanent construction site, the facility may be provided with the help of transportable "housing" fitted with necessary welfare facilities.

**Figure 12.1** An example of a waterless cleaning system with sanitising facility mounted in a fire engine. This waterless cleaning system comprises a cleaner, moisturiser and a sanitising agent. It is designed for outdoor workers (e.g. sewer systems repairers, mobile waste handling crews and other types of mobile workers who may need regular cleaning and sanitising during the working day).
*Photograph: courtesy of Deb Ltd., Belper, Derbyshire, England, UK.*

## SKIN CARE

Skin care is a necessary part of adequate exposure control measures. Regular cleaning will help to remove debris, hazardous agents and sweat. The success of a skin care regime will be influenced by the skin care system in place.

### Selection of a Skin Care System

When selecting a skin care system, it is prudent to take account of the following.

- Skin cleansing products are able to do the job with minimum harm to the skin. For example, skin cleansers without solvents and aggressive scrubbing agents are better than those containing them. It means that the work should be planned and arranged so as to minimise the extent of skin contamination. A consideration should be given to the development of adequate safe working distance (SWD) between hazardous agents/wet-work and the skin. Examples illustrating the application of SWD are described in Chapters 9 and 10.

- The supplier of the system is able to support the performance claims made on the products, preferably with the test results obtained by an independent laboratory.

- Skin care products can be located where they can be easily accessed. For example, pre-work creams should be placed closer to work stations rather than in a remote toilet.

- Products can meet the needs of outdoor and peripatetic workers, where necessary. A waterless cleaning system is better than a running water system for engineering vans, dust carts and emergency vehicles. A number of suppliers have developed innovative approaches to meet user demands. An example of a typical system with cleaning, sanitising and moisturising facilities is shown in Figure 12.1. Another approach to waterless cleaning is shown in Figure 12.2.

- The system can be used without the potential for cross contamination and can meet the demands of work situations. Dispensers are available for personal and community based use, as shown in Figure 12.3.

- The products cause minimum impact to the environment.

- The products cause minimum damage to drainage systems (e.g. minimum or no blockages in pipes).

- Hand rinsing/cleaning facility is suited to the purpose. For example, running hot and cold water through a mixing tap, at a permanent site, to deliver warm water. This arrangement is better than two separate taps requiring water to be mixed in a sink bowl.

- Hand drying facility is kind to the skin. It is practicable to select hand drying facilities which minimise the use of hot air or avoiding the need to use rough papers.

**Figure 12.3**

**A** is showing an example of a personal dispensing system for skin moisturising. Skin cleansers and sanitisers are also available in this format.

**B** is showing an example cleaning station for use at a permanent worksite.

*Photograph A: Courtesy of Degussa-Stoko, Milton Keynes, Buckinghamshire, England, UK. Photograph B: Courtesy of Deb Ltd., Belper, Derbyshire, England, UK.*

**Figure 12.2** This figure is showing an example of a 'waterless' wipe cleaning system in use. These wipes incorporate suitable cleaning agents. Waterless wipe cleaning systems are also useful for wipe cleaning contaminated gloves (before being taken off), surfaces and tools.
*Photograph: Courtesy of Degussa-Stoko, Milton Keynes, Buckinghamshire, England, UK.*

## SKIN CARE PRODUCTS

There is a wide variety of skin care products on the market and they come in many shapes and forms (e.g. gels, liquids, pastes). They differ in efficacy and quality. Skin care products can be placed into the following categories.

- Pre-work creams
- Skin cleansers
- Drying products
- Moisturising creams or after-work creams
- Sanitising products

### Pre-Work Creams

Pre-work creams are formulated with the intention of providing some degree of protection to the skin from various agents such as chemicals, water, micro-organisms and ultra violet (UV) radiation from the sun. Pre-work creams are often called 'barrier creams'. This terminology is incorrect and the reasons for it are given below. Health and safety professionals do not use this terminology and should encourage others to follow their lead.

### How Effective are Pre-Work Creams?

The barrier efficacy of pre-work creams has been tested by a number of independent scientists. They found that the extent of the barrier effect varies from one product to another, even if they are formulated to do the same job.

However, pre-work creams are unlikely to provide a total barrier protection to the skin for the following reasons.

- Pre-work creams are not designed, tested and certified to be sold as personal protective equipment (PPE).

- The manufacturer of a pre-work cream may not be able to guarantee that the product will provide a total barrier against named or mixtures of chemicals or wet-work when used in accordance with their instructions.

- Pre-work cream layer on the skin is susceptible to chemical and water penetration. Manufacturers seldom publish performance data which are independently verified. The term "penetration" is explained in Chapter 11.

- Pre-work creams will allow permeation of chemicals (the term "permeation" is explained in Chapter 11). Manufacturers do not publish scientifically tested permeation data, whether obtained in a laboratory test or at a workplace. The extent of chemical permeation rate through a pre-work cream layer, on the skin, is expected to be significantly faster than those observed through chemical protective gloves.

- Like gloves, there are no universal pre-work creams.

- Workers may not apply the cream to cover the whole area of the skin on hands and forearms. Often certain areas of the hands and wrists are left uncovered as shown in Figure 12.4. This picture was obtained with a help of a cream dosed with a dye, which fluoresces under UV light.

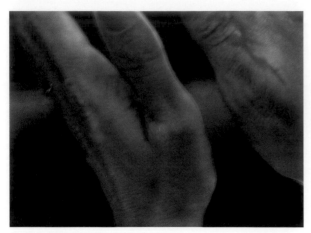

**Figure 12.4** Incomplete application of skin care creams. The effect is shown with the help of a cream dosed with a fluorescent tracer. The areas of the hands without fluorescence have been missed during the application. In order for pre-work creams and moisturisers to work effectively they should be applied to cover the whole area.

**Figure 12.5** This example shows heavy soiling on the skin. Contamination to this extent, by hazardous chemicals, will suggest that hands have been used as a tool; there is a lack of adequate safe working distance and a failure to implement adequate control of dermal exposure.

- The thickness of the cream layer on the hands is inconsistent and cannot be controlled or monitored cost effectively.

- The cream layer on the skin may be damaged or removed during work. Actions such as abrasion, stretching, rubbing and washing can accelerate the removal process.

In summary, pre-work creams <u>are not</u> PPE. They are not designed or tested as PPE and do not function as such. Therefore, pre-work creams should never be used in place of, or as a replacement for, suitable PPE. In other words, pre-work creams are not invisible gloves.

### Is There a Place for Pre-Work Creams in Skin Care?

Pre-work creams can play an important role in a skin care programme. To achieve positive benefits, they should be selected correctly and the areas of the skin needing the protection should be coated with a film of suitable pre-work cream. If these recommendations are observed, pre-work creams could provide limited protection against wet-work, some types of oils and certain chemicals. Dirt and soiling on the skin could be removed easily and without the need for strong cleansing agents including solvents. Regular use is likely to help promote improved personal hygiene practices and should help to maintain skin hydration.

The disadvantage is that some workers may consider that a layer of pre-work cream on their hands works as an 'invisible glove'. This myth should be dispelled using the arguments listed above and practical demonstrations to show the effects illustrated in Figure 12.4. The 'invisible glove' culture could lead to a false sense of security leading to unnecessary skin exposure to chemicals and wet-work.

Another, important factor is that these creams are not designed to provide protection against heavy and uncontrolled soiling of the skin. It should be noted that uncontrolled exposure and heavy soiling of the skin, as shown in Figure 12.5, will indicate that the employer has not implemented adequate exposure protection measures as required by law. It is an indication that the need to implement adequate SWD has not featured in the selection of control strategies.

At present there are no national or international standards for assessing the efficacy of pre-work creams.

### Types of Pre-Work Creams

There are several types of pre-work creams. These may be described as:

- Vanishing creams - these are formulated to trap specified contaminants. In theory, if applied and used correctly, contaminants should not reach the skin surface and the trapped contaminants can be washed-off easily.

- Water-resistant creams - these creams should leave a thin film on the surface of the skin causing it to repel water molecules and water-soluble chemicals.

- Oil/organic solvents resistant creams - these are designed to repel oils, tar and specified organic solvents.

- Converter creams - certain pre-work creams may be formulated to chemically react with the contaminant. In this way the harmful effects of the contaminant is nullified. These creams are difficult to design and the extent of choice and availability limited.

The rapid progress in nano-technology and the technological advances in product formulation may lead to more effective pre-work creams in the future. Some of the future products may well contain visible indicators which will provide in-situ information about the extent of skin contact with chemicals. Any progress in this area should be coupled with independent verification of penetration and permeation capabilities of contaminants against which performance claims are made.

## Guidance for Selecting and Using Pre-Work Creams

- The pre-work cream is capable of providing a degree of protection against hazardous agents (e.g. water, oils, grease, general soil, UV rays) as specified by the manufacturer;

- The supplier of the cream is able to provide information about the extent of expected protection and is supported by data on efficacy;

- The product is dermatologically tested for skin compatibility for general use. However, people with prevailing skin conditions may require some help from an expert (e.g. an occupational hygienist). During routine use, skin checks should be carried out to ensure pre-work creams are not themselves causing any skin problems. Skin checking procedures are explained in Chapter 13;

- The product meets the requirements of relevant cosmetic products regulations;

- The product has been subjected to a production quality assurance programme;

- The product contains only the approved preservatives and anti-microbial agents. These are necessary for protection against product degradation and microbial activities;

- The product contains only the approved perfumes and fragrances. Perfumes and fragrances are often added to increase user acceptance.

- The product is actively supported by the supplier. It means that the supplier is willing to provide educational, training and technical support on skin care management.

Pre-work cream on the skin should be washed off after each work period and when breaks are taken or as recommended by the supplier. A fresh film should be applied before the work recommences.

## Skin Cleansers

It is important to remove contaminants from the skin as often as possible, especially when breaks are taken (e.g. before using the toilets and urinals, smoking, drinking and eating) and at the end of the working day. Water alone will not remove all contaminants (e.g. chemicals, general soil, sweat and salt) from the skin, whereas skin cleansers are designed to remove contaminants from the skin surface. The effectiveness and the ease of cleansing are

achieved by purpose-orientated formulations.

For practical purposes, there are two types of cleansers: soaps and non-soap types. A number of components may be added to a cleanser including the following:

- Scrubbing agents
- Solvents
- Moisturisers
- Emollients
- Preservatives
- Colour formers
- Consistency regulators
- Sequestering agents
- pH adjusters
- Anti-bacterial chemicals
- Fragrances and perfumes

Soaps are made from fats and oils by treating them with a strong alkali such as sodium hydroxide. Soaps are good cleansers because of their ability to act as emulsifying agents, which loosen oil and grease from the skin for rinsing.

Other types of cleansers are formulated with a variety of natural and synthetic surfactants. These can be based on organic and inorganic surfactants or a mixture of both.

Organic solvents may be added to the formulation to remove stubborn contaminants such as paints, lacquers, resins and adhesives. In general, the regular use of solvent- based systems will increase the potential for dermatitis.

Scrubbing agents play a part in mechanically (abrasive or grinding action) dislodging the dirt from the skin surface. The surfactant then attracts the loosened dirt, which is washed away during the rinsing cycle. Commercial competition means claims and counter claims will be made about the usefulness or disadvantages of a particular type of scrubbing agent. A variety of scrubbing agents are used in industrial cleaners including the following:

- Pumice
- Sand
- Cornmeal flour
- Wall nutshell powder
- Coconut shell powder
- Plastic granules

If there is a reason to select cleaners with solvents and/or scrubbing agents, there is a need to ask questions such as:

- What factors are causing significant and ingrained skin contamination?

- What are the reasons for direct skin contact with hazardous agents?

- Are the exposure control systems in place adequate and suitable for minimising skin contamination?

- What are the reasons for not establishing an adequate SWD between the hazardous agent and the skin?

## Guidance for Selecting the Right Skin Cleanser

Although soaps are excellent cleansers, they have disadvantages. Soaps may cause irritation and drying effects on the skin. They can also combine with calcium and magnesium found on the surface of the skin and water. The resulting chemicals can cause irritation to the skin, leave a scum on surfaces and can cause drain blockage. Highly acidic or alkaline soaps may affect the skin's "acid mantle" protection (see Chapter 1), leading to the potential for dry skin, dermatitis and microbial infections.

In general, non-soap based products are milder in comparison to soaps. However, some surfactants, used in non-soap products, have been found to cause skin irritation and/or sensitisation. Some scrubbing agents can cause mechanical damage to the skin surface.

The trick is to choose a cleanser that is effective but as kind as possible to the skin barrier layer. There is no simple answer but the following will provide a guide for selecting the right cleanser. The list below may be used as a checklist when purchasing a skin cleanser.

- The product will do the job with less harm to the skin;

- pH of the product is close to the pH of the skin;

- The product has been subjected to skin compatibility testing, including industry standard allergenic testing. This type should help to protect the majority of users. Those with prevailing skin conditions may require some help from an expert (e.g. an occupational health doctor);

- The product meets the requirements of relevant cosmetic products regulations;

- The product has been subjected to a production quality assurance programme;

- The product is free of organic solvents. Some products contain organic solvents for removing heavy and difficult to remove soiling. If there is a need to choose products containing organic solvents or aggressive cleaning agents, the employer should address the four questions listed in the section above. Actions taken to address the questions should lead to less aggressive cleansers;

- The product does not contain scrubbing agents. Ensure skin contamination is minimised by other control methods so that a cleanser without scrubbing agents could be used. If considering a product with scrubbing agents then justify the need to use such a product and select the one with less abrasive action. Some scrubbing agents can settle in drains and can cause blockages.

- The product contains only the approved preservatives and anti-microbial agents. These are necessary for protection against product degradation and microbial activities;

- The product contains only the approved perfumes and fragrances. Perfumes and fragrances are added to increase user acceptance of cleaning products;

- The product leaves no deposits in drains. This will help to prevent drain blockages;

- The product uses a suitable dispensing system. It should deliver the right amount at the first attempt. The system should not allow cross contamination, cause blockages to the dispensing nozzle or generate drips after dispensing;

- The product is actively supported by the supplier. It means that the supplier is willing to provide educational, training and technical support on skin care management.

## Drying Products

The skin should always be properly dried after washing in warm water. The preferred option should be a soft material with good water absorption characteristics. It is not always practical to use this ideal approach. In such circumstances, the material chosen should causes minimum abrasion to the skin and should easily reach areas between the fingers.

Warm air dryers are common in many work places. The temperature should be set to be warm (not hot) to effect the removal of excess water. Dryers using high velocity air may also be used. Future designs may incorporate a facility for automatically dispensing a measured amount of a moisturiser.

## Moisturisers

For the skin to function as an effective barrier, it should be healthy and remain hydrated to the required levels. The skin barrier layer should contain oils and at least 10-15% water.

The primary role of moisturisers is to replace lost oils and hydrate the skin so as to help maintain the barrier property. The effectiveness of moisturisers varies very widely. Moisturisers are known by different names such as after-work creams and skin conditioners. They come in various forms including creams, lotions and ointments. The basic components of a moisturising cream are water, oils and emulsifiers. Preservatives, anti-bacterial agents, fillers, fragrances and perfumes may be added.

Certain types of work premises (e.g. catering, food processing, micro-electronics) may only permit an 'approved' type. This stipulation may be in force to protect the product being manufactured, made or used.

## Guidance for Selecting Moisturisers

The factors listed below should help select the right product.

- The product is subjected to skin compatibility testing, including allergenic testing. This will protect the majority of users. Those with prevailing skin conditions may require some help from an expert (e.g. an occupational hygienist).

- The product meets all the requirements of relevant cosmetic products regulations.

- The production process is subjected to a quality assurance programme.

- The product is free of alcohol and lanolin. Where practical avoid these products. Alcohol can cause drying effect. Lanolin is known to cause skin sensitisation. For most work situations, it is practicable to choose alternative products.
  *Note: there are products based on lanolin derivatives. These products should not release free lanolin during use.*

- The product does not leave excess grease on the skin after application in accordance with the supplier's information. Users should be given opportunities to try out different products so that they can select the product preferred by the majority.

- Avoid products that take a long time (e.g. minutes) to be absorbed by the skin.

- Choose products containing approved preservatives and anti-microbial agents.

- Perfumes and fragrances based products should only contain approved perfumes and fragrances.

- Avoid products that leave deposits in drains. This may cause blockages.

- The product is actively supported by the supplier. It means that the supplier is willing to provide educational, training and technical support on skin care management.

## Sanitising Products

Increasing use of hand rubs for disinfection in health care environments has led to the development of a large number of alcohol-based hand hygiene products. They have been found to be effective in controlling cross infection, when used correctly. They are easy to use when compared to water-based hand cleaning procedure. Due to the ease of application, they help to improve compliance with hand hygiene standards.

Alcohols (e.g. ethyl and isopropyl alcohols) are well known dehydrating agents. To lessen this effect, hand rub formulations often contain a suitable emollient. However, there is concern that alcohol-based hand rubs may lead to irritant contact dermatitis (ICD) among health care workers. The following procedures should help to minimise the potential for ICD.

- Choosing hand rubs that contain emollients.

- Appling the rub when hands are dry to increase the effectiveness of emollients.

- Developing site specific guidance for the use of hand rubs so as to minimise excessive and unnecessary use of the rubs.

- Improving other hygiene measures to minimise cross contamination.

- Where practical, using mild hand cleaners and warm water for maintaining clean hands.

- Appling moisturisers during breaks.

- Where practical, developing a policy for using disposable gloves in place of hand rubs.

- Considering what additional measures will be needed to protect people with sensitive skin (e.g. regular skin inspection).

## TRAINING AIDS

Training aids have an important role in ensuring good personal hygiene practices. A UV light box (Figure 8.11) and skin care creams dosed with fluorescent dyes are useful for demonstrating the correct application of hand creams and rubs and the correct procedure for hand washing. Posters for promoting the correct hand cleaning procedures and the correct application of skin care creams are available from regulators and suppliers. An example is shown in Figure 12.6. This poster is available for free download from the Health and Safety Executive's 'Skin at Work' website.

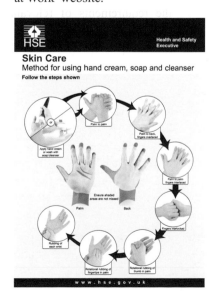

**Figure 12.6**

A poster showing the correct application of skin cleansers and hand cleaning. This poster is available free for download from the Health and Safety Executive's (HSE) 'Skin at Work' website.

## CONCLUSION

The requirement for providing suitable welfare facilities, including skin care systems, is enshrined in law. A good standard of personal hygiene plays an important role in reducing occupational skin diseases. Skin care products are an essential part of personal skin care management at work. There are many products on the market. This Chapter provides guidance for the selection and use of skin care products.

Skin contamination by chemicals and wet-work should be prevented or adequately controlled. Pre-work creams will not provide a 100% barrier and they are not PPE. However, they have a role in skin care management at work. Waterless cleaning and sanitising systems are gaining popularity and they have an important place in skin care management at work. Alcohol-based sanitising products may present a risk to the skin: their use should be actively managed to reduce the potential for skin diseases.

## TEST YOUR KNOWLEDGE

1. Explain why pre-work creams can not be relied upon for total barrier function.

2. Describe the essential components of a common sense personal hygiene system at work.

3. Skin care systems alone cannot be relied upon for adequate control of exposure to chemicals and wet-work. Discuss.

## FURTHER READING

**Choice of skin care products for the workplace.** HSE Books, Sudbury, UK. ISBN: 9 780717 618255.

**Dermal absorption of isopropyl alcohol from a commercial hand rub: implications for its use in hand decontamination.** P Turner, B Saeed, MC Kelsey. Journal of Hospital Infection; 56 (2004):287-290.

**Dermatological aspects of a successful introduction and continuation of alcohol-based hand rubs for hygienic hand disinfection.** G Kampf, H Loffler. Journal of Hospital Infection; 55 (2003):1-7.

**Effectiveness of barrier cream for controlling exposure: Final Report.** P Simpson, J Wheeler, M Roff. Health and Safety Laboratory, Buxton, UK.

**Efficacy of skin barrier creams.** PJ Frosch, A Schulze-Dirks, M Hoffmann, I Axthelm. Contact Dermatitis; 29 (1993):74-77.

**Evaluation of barrier creams – introduction and comparison of 3 in vivo methods.** T Rieger, A Teichmann, H Richter, S Schanzer, w Sterry, J Lademann. Contact Dermatitis; 56 (2007): 347-354.

**Evaluation of barrier creams against sulphur mustard.** RP Chilcot, J Jenner, SAM Hotchkiss, P Rice. Skin Pharmacology and Applied Skin Physiology; 15 (2002):225-235.

**Moisturizer effect on irritant dermatitis: an overview.** M Yokota, HI Maibach. Contact Dermatitis; 55 (2006):65-72.

**Occupational skin-care management.** TL Diepgen and H Maibach. International Archives of Occupational and Environmental Health; 76 (2003): 323-324.

**Occupational skin-protection products – a review.** J Kresken, A Klotz. International Archives of Occupational and Environmental Health; 76 (2003): 355- 358.

**Prevention of poison oak allergic contact dermatitis by quaternium-18 bentonite.** JG Marks et al. Journal of the American Academy of Dermatologists; 33 (1995):212-216.

**Problems with trials and intervention studies on barrier creams and emollients at the workplace.** PJ Coenraads, TL Diepgen. International Archives of Occupational and Environmental Health; 76 (2003): 362-366.

**Skin cleansers for occupational use: testing the skin compatibility of different formulations.** A Klotz, M Veeger, W Rocher. International Archives of Occupational and Environmental Health; 76 (2003):367-373.

**Skin condition associated with intensive use of alcoholic gels for hand disinfection: a combination of biophysical and sensorial data.** E Hoban, K De Peeped, V Rogers. Contact Dermatitis; 54 (2006): 261-267.

**Skin-conditioning products in occupational dermatology.** P Elsner, W Wigger-Alberti. International Archives of Occupational and Environmental Health; 76 (2003): 351-354.

**Sunscreen's weakness brought to light.** Chemistry World. October 2006: 32.

**The effectiveness of barrier creams in protecting against dermatitis: a pilot study.** M Parkinson, JW Cherrie. Human exposure research organisations exchange (HEROX). University of Aberdeen. www.abdn.ac.uk

**The prevention of nickel contact dermatitis: a review of the use of binding agents and barrier creams.** DJ Gowkrodger, J Healy, AM Howe. Contact Dermatitis; 32 (1995):257-265.

**The Workplace (Health, Safety and Welfare) Regulations 1992.** Statutory Instrument 1992 No.3004. HM Stationary Office. London, UK.

**Tolerance and acceptability of 14 surgical and hygienic alcohol-based hand rubs.** R Girard, E Bousquet, E Carre et al. Journal of Hospital Infection; 63 (2006):281-288.

*Chapter 13*

# Checking for Early Signs of Disease

## INTRODUCTION

Every year, many thousands of people are made ill at work. The pain, distress and the costs associated with work-related ill health can be minimised by taking effective exposure control actions on time. Regular checking for early signs of disease forms part of the control actions. It can deliver a number of advantages for employers, employees, shareholders, health services, and the relatives of those affected by work-related ill health.

Checking for early signs of diseases is the third part of the APC approach described in Chapter 9. The technical term for "checking for early signs of a disease" is health surveillance (HS). It uses a variety of early detection techniques and procedures. These include: skin condition monitoring, visual examination of the skin by a competent person, self-checks, biological monitoring, biological effects monitoring and an assessment or an examination by a medically qualified person.

The main purpose of this Chapter is to provide guidance for the early detection of skin diseases caused by dermal exposure to chemicals and *wet-work*.

## HEALTH SURVEILLANCE

### What is It?

Health surveillance is about putting in place appropriate procedures:

1. To detect early signs of work-related ill health (e.g. contact dermatitis, vibration white finger, asthma) or adverse effects or changes in the body (e.g. redness of the skin, tingling feelings in the fingers, reduction in lung function) which may be caused by exposure to *hazardous agents*;

2. For taking control actions on the basis of the findings at 1, above; and

3. For keeping individual health records. The records may include medical-in-confidence information securely kept by a medically qualified person.

Certain types of checks and tests are not directly relevant for the early detection of a work-related disease. Therefore, they are not HS. Examples include:

● Health promotion activities such as advice on eating a balanced diet, giving up smoking, sensible use of alcohol and other well-being programmes such as yoga classes.

● Annual health checks forming part of employee benefit schemes.

● Checking for misuse of alcohol or other drugs, unless there are safety-critical implications (e.g. operating a tower crane).

### Benefits

HS is aimed at protecting the health of individual employees. It brings benefits to the employers, employees, shareholders, heath services, and the relatives of those affected by work-related ill health. The benefits of HS include:

● Helping to identify, as early as possible, any indications of a disease or adverse effects;

● Enabling steps to be taken to treat those affected. For example, treating contact dermatitis;

● Helping to advise about future health preservation strategies. This will include assessing the need to remove the person from the environment causing the exposure. For example, taking preventive actions when a person has become sensitised to epoxy resins;

● Helping to assess any deficiencies in current exposure control measures;

● Helping to initiate corrective actions to restore adequate control of exposure by all routes, as necessary;

● Helping to assess the long term effectiveness of control measures;

● Providing an opportunity to re-train and instruct employees so that safe working practices can be restored. For example, how to prevent internal contamination of gloves.

- Giving employees an opportunity to discuss any concerns about the effect of their work on their health;

- Helping to reduce lost time and lost production;

- Helping to reduce the cost burden to health services, employees and employers; and

- Helping to reduce pain and suffering amongst employees and to minimise effects on their relatives.

**Where HS is Appropriate**

HS is appropriate when:

- An employee is exposed to a hazardous agent and

- The agent is known to be associated with an identifiable disease or an adverse effect and

- There is a reasonable likelihood that the disease or the adverse effect may occur under the particular conditions of the work and

- A *valid technique* is available for detecting the early signs of the disease or the adverse effect and

- The technique used is unlikely to place employees at an increased risk or to cause unacceptable harm to the employees and

- The HS procedure undertaken is likely to benefit the employee.

The requirements described above are explained using an example. During construction work, bricklayers' skin comes into contact with wet cement and the contact causes irritation and dryness of the skin (adverse effects) and the exposure can lead to irritant and/or allergic contact dermatitis (the identifiable disease) under the conditions of work and it is reasonably practicable to detect the disease early by regular skin inspections (valid technique) and the skin inspection is unlikely to increase the risk of dermatitis or cause any other harm to the bricklayers.

The minimum required HS procedure may be mandated or recommended in law. For example, where there is exposure to a substance known to cause severe dermatitis and the exposure is likely to cause the disease, the COSHH *Approved Code of Practice* recommends skin inspection by a "responsible person" (defined in the section "who can carry out HS"). Table 13.1 lists examples of substances known to cause skin diseases and suggested procedures for HS. Employees exposed to these substances should be subjected to HS, when the conditions for HS are met. Employers should also consult other relevant resources including Table 4.1.

**When it is not required?**

HS is not required where there is no exposure; when the exposure is rare, short and at very low concentrations. As a guide HS is not required when the exposure levels are consistently well below inhalation occupational exposure limits for airborne exposure and below the total daily dermal contamination levels given in Table 8.2.

**PRACTICAL APPROACHES TO DETERMINING THE NEED**

A number of practical approaches will help to assess whether HS might be appropriate. These include:

**(i) Previous Cases of Work-Related Ill Health**

Previous history or cases of work-related skin disease, which is associated with a particular chemical, product or process, will suggest that there could be a possibility of future cases. For example, dermatitis in epoxy resins manufacturing.

**(ii) Outbreak of a Disease**

A sudden outbreak of skin disease, at a workplace, (e.g. dermatitis among a group of printers) will indicate that the disease may be work-related. This type of situation should initiate an investigation to establish the causes of control failures and may also involve immediate HS of exposed workers.

**(iii) Disease Surveillance Procedures**

Enforcement authorities operate work-related disease-monitoring schemes. They are designed to monitor trends and developments. For example, GB-EPIDERM database, on skin diseases, provides information about latex rubber protein allergies among single-use disposable latex glove users in the National Health Service and elsewhere. This information led to new advice on single-use disposable latex gloves. It included enforcement guidelines for risk reduction measures which includes HS.

Other sources of information include insurers, trades unions and trade associations. Safety data sheets may also provide this information.

**(iv) Sickness Absence Management**

This does not fall within the strictest definition of HS, but it has an important place in risk reduction arrangements. It is important to know the cause of an employee's sickness, in case it is work-related. If it is, employer will have to put in place measures to minimise the risks. The improved control measures may involve regular HS (e.g. six monthly HS).

**Table 13.1** Substances and health surveillance procedures

| Substance | Typical HS procedure |
|---|---|
| Substances known to cause severe dermatitis. See Table 4.1, Health and Safety Executive (HSE) Guidance Note MS24 and other guides published by regulatory agencies. Chemicals and products carrying the hazard phrases R38, R43, and R66. | Skin inspection by a responsible person. Employers may choose to employ an occupational health specialist to do the job. |
| Substances known to cause skin sensitisation. Chemicals and products carrying the hazard phrase R43, those listed in MS24 and Table 4.1. | Skin inspection by a responsible person. In some cases, medical surveillance and patch testing may be recommended by an occupational health specialist. |
| Substances known to cause depigmentation (e.g. alkyl phenols such as hydroquinone) | Skin inspection by a responsible person. Employers may choose to employ an occupational health specialist to do the job. |
| Substances known to cause oil acne (e.g. certain types of cutting oils) and chloracne (e.g. dibenzodioxins) | Skin inspection by a responsible person. Employers may choose to employ an occupational health specialist to do the job. |
| Wet-work (for explanation see Glossary of Terms in Appendix 1) | Skin inspection by a responsible person. Employers may choose to employ an occupational health specialist to do the job. |
| Substance which may cause skin cancer. Chemicals and products carrying the hazard phrase R40. | Medical surveillance. |
| Substances that can be taken up via the unbroken skin. Chemicals with skin notation (Table 4.2), chemicals and products carrying hazard phrases R21, R24, R27, R39/24, R39/27, R48/24, R68/21. | Biological monitoring or biological effect monitoring (when suitable and validated methods are available). |
| Manufacture, production, reclamation, storage, discharge, transport, use or polymerisation of vinyl chloride monomer. | Medical surveillance. |
| Nitro or amino derivatives of phenol and of benzene or its homologues (having a similar structure; e.g. Nitrotoluene). Manufacturing, including the manufacture of explosives using these substances. | Medical surveillance. |
| Manufacture of potassium or sodium chromate or dichromate. | Medical surveillance. |
| Manufacture and use of ortho-toluidine and its salts; Dianisidine and its salts; Dichlorobenzidine and its salts. | Medical surveillance. |
| Manufacture of auramine and magenta. | Medical surveillance. |
| Carbon disulphide. Disulphur dichloride, benzene, including benzol. Carbon tetrachloride. Trichloroethylene. Process in which these substances are used or given off as vapour or in the manufacture of rubber or articles or goods made wholly or partially of rubber. | Medical surveillance. |
| Pitch. Manufacture of blocks of fuel consisting of coal, coal dust, coke or slurry with pitch as a binding substance. | Medical surveillance. |

## FREQUENCY OF HEALTH SURVEILLANCE

Some regulations will stipulate the intervals at which HS should be carried out. For example, COSHH regulations stipulate that for substances listed in Schedule 6, employees should be subjected to medical surveillance at intervals of not more than twelve months.

Where the intervals and frequencies are not stipulated in law, employers should determine the frequency on the basis of a suitable and sufficient risk assessment. Further guidance and advice on specific substances and process may be available from enforcement authorities.

HS is an aid; the primary approach should be prevention or minimisation of exposure to chemicals and wet-work. Where dermatitis is a known and widespread problem among a particular workforce (e.g. hair dressers, epoxy workers), it is sensible to implement weekly self-checks and monthly skin inspection by a responsible person. If the problem has been brought under control and the controls are sustained over a long period, the frequency may be reduced to once every six or twelve months.

## WHO CAN CARRY OUT HEALTH SURVEILLANCE?

### Self-Checks

Self-checks have an important place in detecting early signs of work-related dermatitis. The poster shown in Figure 13.1 provides help for self-checks. In its simplest form, employees may check themselves for signs or symptoms of dermatitis. Self-checks should be carried out as part of an existing HS programme under the

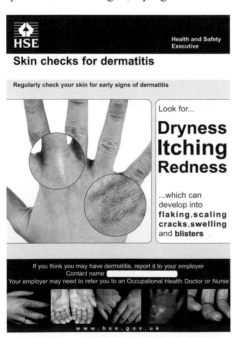

**Figure 13.1** A poster illustrating the approaches for skin self checks for early detection of work-related dermatitis. This poster is available free for download from the Health and Safety Executive's 'Skin at Work' website.

supervision of a responsible person. For self-checks to be effective, employees should be trained on what to look for and know to whom they should report any symptoms. They should have confidence that corrective actions will be put in place where necessary and this will take place in the context of a "no blame" culture.

### Responsible Person

A responsible person is one appointed by the employer, is competent to carry out assessments for early signs of a disease and is charged with reporting to the employer the findings of the procedure. This person may be a supervisor, foreman, first-aider, safety representative or the employer.

In general, a responsible person would carry out HS for dermatitis; ulceration of the skin caused by metals and for early skin changes associated with work-related skin ***depigmentation.***

Typical duties of a responsible person are illustrated with the help of how to identify early signs of dermatitis. Where there is a risk of dermatitis, the responsible person is expected to:

- Carry out skin condition assessment prior to someone joining the company or as soon as possible after an employee has started the work;

- Carry out periodic checking of the hands and forearms of employees for early signs of dermatitis;

- Keep health records of the skin checks;

- Inform the employer of the outcomes of skin checks so that he or she can take necessary actions;

- Advise employer to seek expert help for managing any outbreak of dermatitis and for restoring adequate control of exposure.

The responsible person may carry out skin inspection by direct observation of the skin, using a questionnaire or some other method within his/her competence. To be competent, the person should know:

(i)   Which processes, substances or products at their work are associated with the potential to cause skin disease. This information can be found in regulatory, industry sector and trade association publications. Tables 13.1 and 4.1 should also provide help.

(ii)  The types of skin conditions (e.g. redness and cracking) and diseases (e.g. irritant contact dermatitis, allergic contact dermatitis, skin cancer, skin discolorations and boils) that may be caused by the substance in question.

(iii) How exposures take place (i.e. knowledge on handling, use procedures and dermal exposure pathways).

(iv) The control measures that should be in place to prevent or adequately control dermal exposure?

(v) The types of shortcomings in control measures that are likely to cause dermal exposure and the extent of risks in their particular workplace. For example: inadequate design or incorrect use of extract ventilation systems; contamination of work surfaces; surfaces are not cleaned routinely; skin comes into contact with contaminated tools, equipment and clothing; contamination of the insides of gloves (because wearers have not been instructed on correct use); using heavily contaminated coveralls and/or apron; no procedure in place for regularly cleaning reusable protective clothing; contamination on footwear contributing to skin contamination.

(vi) The early visible signs of dermatitis. The signs include: redness, itching, swelling, minor scaling, severely dry looking skin without shine and luster, discoloration and minor wounds.

(vii) What should be done if controls are not working and/or signs of skin problems are noted. These will include: reporting to the employer that signs on the skin have given cause for concern; requesting that the person should be seen by a medical practitioner (this could be the individual's General Practitioner) as soon as is practicable; keeping a record of what was observed and to whom that record belongs; and reporting to the employer any incorrect use/the lack of controls. Once the report is made, the employer should investigate, reinstate adequate exposure control measures and make arrangements for medical assistance so that the affected person can receive help.

## Medically Qualified Person

A medically qualified person will include general practitioners, occupational health physicians, occupational health nurses and other specialist doctors such as dermatologists. However, the person should be competent to assess work-related ill health problems and

should have an understanding of the process; hazardous substances involved in the process; dermal exposure pathways and exposure control measures. They should know when to seek help from other experts such as safety managers and occupational hygienists.

## RECORDS

### Health Record

Employers should keep up-to-date health records of HS for each employee undergoing HS. The health record will contain non-clinical data, which means the contents of a health record are not medical information. However, the record will contain personal data, as shown in Table 13.2. Therefore, the information should be treated as personal information.

Employees have the right to see their health records. With the consent of an affected employee, health records should be made available to the employees' representatives such as a trade union representative. An authorised representative from the relevant enforcement authority (e.g. HM Inspector of Health and Safety) may ask to view the records.

The length of time a health record should be kept varies from one country to another. In the UK, it should be kept for 40 years from the date of the last entry made in it. If a firm goes out of business, history shows that the data are lost because there are no centrally operated data banks.

### Medical Record

A typical medical record should be able to identify unequivocally the person to whom it belongs and will also contain the findings of HS, including medical assessments undertaken by a medically qualified person. A HS record incorporating medical information should be treated as medical-in-confidence and the access to the information should be subjected to an established protocol. Confidential clinical records will be held in confidence by a doctor, nurse, or other occupational health professional in a secure place, and not be available to others.

**Table 13.2** Elements of a health record information

| Personal information | Job information | Health surveillance (HS) information |
|---|---|---|
| Surname | | |
| Forenames | | |
| Sex | An historical record of jobs (including the current one) involving exposure to chemicals and wet-work. | History of HS including dates and who carried it out. Fitness to continue to work, if appropriate. |
| Date of Birth | | |
| Permanent address | | The decisions and recommendations of a responsible person, doctor, nurse or an occupational hygienist |
| NI number | | |
| Date started present job | | |

## HEALTH SURVEILLANCE TECHNIQUES

There are a variety of HS techniques and procedures. In every case, the most suitable ones should be selected, based primarily on regulatory recommendations. Other factors influencing the selection of a technique will include: workplace situation, expertise of the person carrying out the technique and benefits to the affected individual. Examples of commonly used techniques and procedures are described below.

### Biological Monitoring

Biological monitoring (BM) does not identify or measure the extent of ill health, but will provide information on adequacy of exposure control. BM is the measurement and assessment of workplace agents or their *metabolites*. Measurements are made either on samples of breath, urine, blood or any combination of these. The technique and its application are detailed in Chapter 8. Taking blood is an invasive procedure and should be avoided where possible.

### Biological Effect Monitoring

Biological effect monitoring (BEM) is the measurement and assessment of early biological effect in exposed workers. For example, established disease markers in blood samples in association with a medical interpretation may be used for assessing health effects or diseases development. Thus, BEM will fall under medical surveillance and the records should be considered as medical-in-confidence.

### Medical Surveillance and Clinical Investigation

These will be carried out by a medically qualified doctor. In some cases, the appointment of this person and the types of clinical examinations to be carried out may be subjected to regulatory requirements. For example, those working with lead may be placed under a medical surveillance programme as determined by the 'appointed doctor' – a medical practitioner appointed in writing by a regulatory authority.

### Skin Inspection

A competent responsible person may carry out skin inspections to detect early signs of work-related dermatitis caused by wet-work and chemicals. A poster published by the HSE provides simple instructions for skin inspection and is shown in Figure 13.1. Some employers may engage the services of a medically qualified person to carry out their routine HS. This person may inform the employer of any additional procedures that will benefit the employees and the organisation.

### Skin Condition Monitoring

For the skin to function as an effective barrier, it should be adequately hydrated. The importance of hydration is discussed in Chapters 1 and 2. In simple terms, the electrical properties of the layers on the outer section of the skin are related to their water content. In the context of skin condition monitoring, a water rich horny layer is highly conductive, whereas a dry horny layer acts as a poor conductor. This means skin condition monitoring can help to detect the potential for skin damage at an early stage. A competent responsible person may carry out skin condition monitoring using a suitable device. There are two commonly used methods: surface hydration (moisture level) monitoring, using a corneometer and the rate of water-loss monitoring, known as trans-epidermal water loss (TEWL).

In corneometric measurements, the capacitance level of the skin is measured which is proportional to the water content. Higher values indicate a more hydrated skin surface. The TEWL technique measures the evaporation rate $(g/m^2h)$ from the horny layer. The measurement

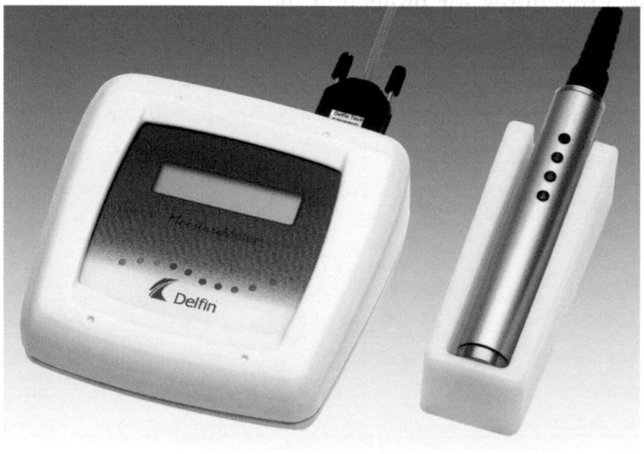

**Figure 13.2** An example of a skin condition monitoring instrument for measuring hydration levels. The probe will be place on the skin to monitor the hydration level. *Photograph: Courtesy of Delfin Technologies Ltd., Kuopio, Finland.*

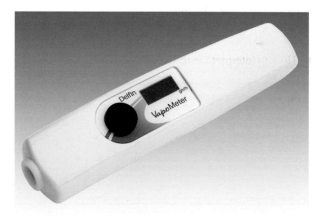

**Figure 13.3** An example of a skin condition monitoring instrument for assessing the rate of water loss from the skin due to evaporation. The extent of water loss can be influenced by many factors including the condition of the skin. *Photograph: Courtesy of Delfin Technologies Ltd., Kuopio, Finland.*

**Table 13.3** A typical scoring system for skin condition monitoring

| SKIN MOISTURE LEVEL | | TRANS-EPIDERMAL WATER LOSS (TEWL) | |
|---|---|---|---|
| Meter reading[A]<br>(Arbitrary units) | Skin condition | Meter reading[B]<br>(Arbitrary units) | Skin condition |
| < 20 | Dry skin | 0-4 | Very healthy skin condition |
| 20 - 40 | Normally hydrated skin | 5-9 | Healthy skin condition |
| > 40 | Well hydrated skin | 10-12 | Normal condition |
| | | 13-15 | Strained skin |
| | | 16-20 | Critical condition |

*Note: A – Units used with Delfin MoistureMeter SC, Delfin Technologies Ltd., Kuopio, Finland. B – Units used by another manufacturer.*

probes are sensitive to air movements and this will influence the results obtained. Therefore, the probes should be used in accordance with the manufacturer's instructions. These techniques are relatively easy to carry out and the monitoring devices are simple and cost effective to use.

Routine use of these monitoring methods can help to establish trends of skin quality. Any apparent deterioration in the quality will trigger an early investigation of the potential causes. Examples of monitoring equipment are shown in Figures 13.2 and 13.3. Table 13.3 shows a typical qualitative scoring system for interpreting the measurement data and to monitor any apparent deterioration in the quality of the skin. Suppliers use different scales and interpretation approaches to suit their equipment design.

## Patch Testing

Patch testing may be required to make a diagnosis of allergic contact dermatitis. Patch testing should only be carried out by those specifically trained in its technique and is usually undertaken in dermatology departments in hospitals by competent personnel. It means the person carrying out the test knows:

● How to carry out the test;

● How to interpret the test results;

● What actions may be necessary on the basis of the results;

● What to do if things go wrong when the test is carried out.

## EMPLOYEE PARTICIPATION

For an HS programme to deliver benefits, it is necessary to have the full co-operation of the employees and their representatives. They should play a part in the development of the programme. Employers should have open and transparent systems on the following issues:

● The aims and objectives of the HS programme;

● Benefits to those being subjected to HS;

● Procedures involved (e.g. skin checks or examination by a doctor);

● The information that will be made available to the employer and in what format (e.g. collective or individual information);

● What will happen to the results and how will it be used;

● The consequences for employment, where there are adverse findings on ill health or signs of ill health;

● Procedures for maintaining the confidentiality of information on individual employees;

● Procedures for monitoring the effectiveness of the programme;

● Procedures for protecting the rights of individuals. Some HS procedures and techniques may involve clinical examination and may include measurements using body fluids (e.g. urine, breath and/or, blood). Those being subjected to the tests should agree to the tests and should provide written consent to carry out the agreed clinical investigation;

● Procedures for implementing the legal requirements for HS.

## CONCLUSION

HS, where necessary, is part of the exposure control strategies required by law. Checking for early signs of a disease can pay dividends to employers and employees. There are many skin HS techniques and procedures. They are useful for detecting early signs of work-related dermatitis. Most techniques are simple and easy to implement. Biological monitoring is useful for substances absorbed via the skin. Skin condition monitoring is useful for detecting the potential for skin damage. Skin inspection by a competent responsible person is required in circumstances where there is a possibility for severe work-related dermatitis. Sickness absence management is a useful tool for identifying, at an early stage, potential for ill health problems caused by work.

## TEST YOUR KNOWLEDGE

1. Explain what you understand by the term health surveillance.

2. When is health surveillance appropriate?

3. Explain the differences between health record and medical record.

4. List 3 health surveillance techniques/procedures and explain their purpose.

5. Explain what factors will encourage you to incorporate health surveillance for preventing work-related dermatitis in your workplace.

## FURTHER READING

**Control of lead at work - Approved Code of Practice.** HSE Books, Sudbury, UK. ISBN: 0 7176 1506 5.

**Control of substances hazardous to health (Fifth edition).** HSE Books, Sudbury, UK. ISBN 0 7176 2981 3.

**Electrical methods for skin moisture assessment.** OG Martinsen, S Grimnes, J Karlsen. Skin Pharmacology; 8 (1995): 237-245.

**Guidance on laboratory techniques in occupational medicine (Tenth Edition; 2005).** Health and Safety Laboratory, Buxton, UK.

**Guidelines for transepidermal water loss (TEWL) measurements. A report from the Standardization Group of the European Society of Contact Dermatitis.** J Pinnagoda, RA Tupker, T Agner, J Serup. Contact Dermatitis; 22 (1990): 164-178.

**Health surveillance for hexavalent chromium compounds.** Surface Engineering Association, Birmingham, UK.

**Health surveillance at work (HSG61).** HSE Books, Sudbury, UK. ISBN: 0 7176 1705 X.

**Management of Health and Safety at Work Approved Code of Practice (L21).** HSE Books, Sudbury, UK. ISBN: 0 11 886330 4.

**Medical Aspects of Occupational Skin Disease. MS24, Second Edition. 2004.** HSE Books, Sudbury, UK. ISBN: 9 780717 615452.

**Study of the stratum corneum barrier function by TEWL measurement.** AO Barel, P Clarys. Skin pharmacology; 8 (1995): 186-195.

**Textbook of Contact Dermatitis.** Editors: RJG Rycroft, T Menné, PJ Frosch, JP Lepoittevin. Springer-Verlag, Berlin, Germany. ISBN 3 540 66842 X.

*Chapter 14*

# Benefits Realisation

## INTRODUCTION

Implementing and maintaining effective risk management arrangements will require sustained behavioural changes at all levels in an organisation. Evidence shows that risky or inappropriate management and work practices can return if safe behaviours are not reinforced through evidence-based management arrangements. Key strategies for changing peoples' behaviours and retaining employee commitment include risk communication, training, employee participation and trust between shop floor and management in all aspects of health and safety risk management and the associated reward systems. An evidence-based management practices will include regular reviews of risk control strategies to ensure that they are delivering the expected outcomes on a long-term basis, root-cause analysis of events (e.g. accidents and injuries and diseases) and absence management.

The aim of this Chapter is to describe some of the key issues associated with learning, good risk communication, training and employee involvement. An appreciation of these issues will help to implement and maintain effective dermal exposure control measures. The issues discussed in this Chapter are equally applicable to other areas of exposure risk control.

## INFORMATION, INSTRUCTION AND TRAINING

### How Do We Learn and Remember?

Learning is an integral part of information, instruction and training (IIT). When people receive IIT, they listen, reflect, store, recall and use the information, experience and knowledge as they see fit. Therefore, when devising arrangements for IIT, providers should aim to maximise learning and persuade the listeners to act in the desired manner. It will help to create an environment for desirable behaviours.

People learn new things in a variety of ways. Research at a secondary school showed that students' top preferences in teaching methods were group discussion, simulation, role-play, experiments, developing practical ideas and artwork. Less effective methods included lectures and theoretical approaches.

A typical relationship between learning methods, sensory routes and recall rates, is pictorially summarised in Figure 14.1. It shows that listening, alone, does not contribute significantly to recall (only about 5%) because it only involves one sensory route – the ears. In contrast, when the learning is achieved by practising a scenario, the recall rate goes up to 75%. In a practice-based approach different types of sensory routes are helping to learn and memorise intended messages. There is a key message for risk communicators and trainers: think critically about the ways in which concepts are communicated and taught. The aim should be to use teaching/communication approaches that involve a mixture of relevant methods as shown at the bottom of the pyramid in Figure 14.1.

The process of remembering involves gaining information through sensory systems, passing them to the short-term memory and from there to the long-term memory. Unless the information stored in the long-term memory is used or recalled regularly in some way, the information may be lost or forgotten. Forgetting may be viewed as the brain's de-cluttering procedure for seldom-used information. The content of the short-term memory is short-lived and is easily replaced by new information. Therefore, as illustrated earlier, IIT should utilise a variety of teaching methods and should involve as many sensory routes as possible. IIT should be directly relevant to the risk reduction arrangements in the workplace so that recall and use of the relevant information takes place regularly. Generalised training on how to select and use chemical protective gloves is less useful than one that is specific to the given workplace. The latter approach will provide many opportunities to recall, reflect, test and use the information, techniques and methods.

The diagram may be summarised in the following way:

**People will remember –**

*A little of what they hear,*

*Some of what they read,*

*Much of what they see*

*More of what they practice, and*

*Almost all of what they understand fully, practice and experience.*

(based on KL Moore and AF Dalley)

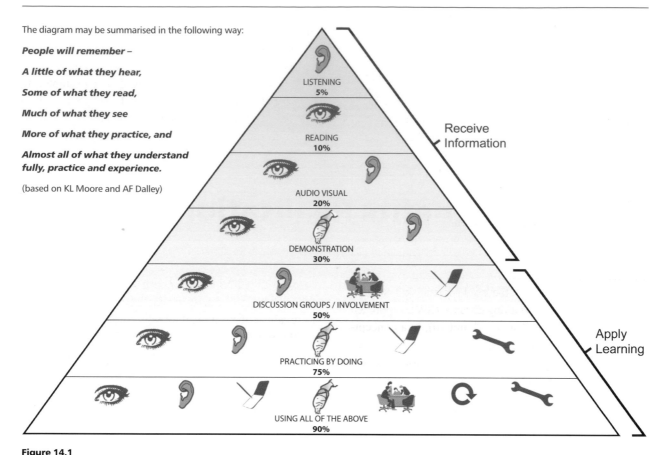

**Figure 14.1**

This illustration shows major types of approaches used in training and communication and the typical recall-rates in percentage. The extent of recall rate increases when a combination of approaches is utilised. This figure is based on E Dale; and G Petty.

## Risk Communication

Risk communication in the main is a passive process and the audience is selective in paying attention to information. They only retain what is perceived as important and the messages received may be distorted. These may happen due to their views, understanding and/or other external influences. However, risk communication is an integral component of risk management. It helps to raise awareness and knowledge, which in turn should minimise unsafe risk perceptions, myths, negative attitudes and risk taking activities. It also helps to bring about and maintain desirable behaviours of the target groups, such as managers, workers and contractors. It is a process by which people share meaning. Effective communication takes place when the participants are able to understand the correct meaning embedded in a message, correctly interpret it and then use it in the right way.

Risk communication should not be used as a "bolt-on" to the overall risk management arrangements. Just providing a collection of information, such as handouts, safety data sheets or an instruction manual, may be considered as bolt-on. Risk communication should help to actively engage those affected by or interested in the risks so that they can share or reflect their views about the hazards; the associated risks; and the consequences of the risks.

In the context of this book, risk communication may be described as the exchange of information and opinions between interested stakeholders about: the nature, magnitude and significance of hazards, how best to minimise health and safety risks in the workplace and the benefits of risk minimisation to individuals, their families, the organisation and the society as a whole.

An effective risk communication will have certain features. These include:

- A maximum of five key messages. Ideally, key messages should be limited to three.

- Attention seeking. This is important because each message or information given out is competing with many other messages or information emanating from different sources on different aspects.

- Communication methods tailored to the needs of the audience.

- Delivery approaches built on a logical framework and relevant to the audience and the risks they face.

- An evaluation to seek responses and feedback from the audience. Ideally, evaluation should take place before and after the event. The purpose is to evaluate the effectiveness of the procedure, learning experiences of the participants and their intention to take action after the event.

## Training

Training helps to improve skills and understanding of the risk control measures. To be effective, it should help to transfer lessons and techniques learnt to perform the work.

A training programme may serve a range of purposes and may be initiated for different reasons. In the context of this book, the purposes of providing training will include: to improve health and safety, worker performance and productivity; to help the trainee to acquire skills and understand concepts; to improve exposure control methods, to understand procedures and rules to deliver a task with *tolerable* risks to health and safety. These attributes should, also, help to change attitudes and maintain the required behaviours. Training may range from developing a highly focussed specific skill, such as how to apply the safe working distance (SWD) approach to a given task, (see Chapters 9 and 10), to a concept-based training, such as leadership skills and developing and managing worker involvement for benefits realisation. Re-training may be used for reinforcing the skills and concepts already learnt. The Health and Safety Executive (HSE) recommends a five-step approach to training. These are:

- Step 1: Decide what training is needed. The main purpose of this step is to identify the skills and knowledge needed to do a job/task/process with tolerable risks to health and safety.

- Step 2: Decide what the training priorities are. This step will help to rank the priority for training on the basis of the extent of the hazard, the risk associated with the hazards and the people involved. For example, the needs of a new process worker will take priority over a long serving employee who is familiar with health and safety risks and the control measures in place.

- Step 3: Choose the training methods and resources. This step will require careful consideration. Some of the important factors needing consideration are explained in previous sections. Additional help is provided in the section below.

- Step 4: Deliver the training. See comments in Step 3, above.

- Step 5: Check that the training has worked. It is essential to seek feedback from the audience and evaluate the practical effectiveness and outcomes of the training. This information will help to improve future training. Evaluation should be undertaken with care and the elements selected for the evaluation should include, as appropriate, tests for understanding, knowledge retention, improvements in skills, behavioural changes, productivity, cost, long term effectiveness of the training for risk reduction measures and measures for improvements in organisation's health and safety performance.

The fundamental purposes of IIT may be summarised using a mnemonic – AIDAR. An explanation of AIDAR is given in Table 14.1.

**Table 14.1** IIT and AIDAR[A]

| | | |
|---|---|---|
| **A** | Awareness | Creating and/or raising awareness about a particular hazard, the risks and the control measures needed. Awareness helps significantly to change attitudes and maintain positive behaviours of the target groups. |
| **I** | Interest | Developing an interest and appreciation of the issues associated with hazard, risks and controls and understanding the need for action. Using practical examples and/or people with personal experience and suffering should help to create an interest. Where practical, involve the workforce when developing arrangements for risk control, including IIT. |
| **D** | Desire | Helping to create an environment and the motivation to take the required actions. |
| **A** | Action | Equipping with skills for using the tools and methods for risk control. Taking actions for implementing control measures and using them correctly in accordance with the IIT provided. |
| **R** | Review; Reward; Root-cause analysis | Reviewing the effectiveness of IIT and implementation of controls. This may involve audits, effectiveness assessment and determining the need and frequency for repeating the AIDAR loop. Assessing the effectiveness of the expected outcomes when risk control measures are working. This would help to reshape control arrangements including IIT. Rewarding performance and improving behaviours. Root-cause analysis aims to prevent undesirable events (e.g. accidents and ill health) in the future and requires a methodical and structured approach to information gathering (evidence), collation of the information, analysis, interpretation and recommendations for way forward. |

**Note:** A - AIDAR concept is based on the models designed by Lewis, Sheldon and Strong. Strong (1925)

## Considerations for Delivering IIT

It is useful to follow some basic rules for maximising engagement, learning and the application of risk reduction measures. Some of the important basic rules for IIT are listed below. The list below does not attempt to separate rules relevant for different aspects of IIT. Readers should adopt key elements relevant to individual situations.

---

✗   Do not cover new information too quickly;

✗   Do not speak too fast;

✓   Do speak clearly;

✓   Leave a silence or a pause after making an important key message. This will provide time for quick reflection and for the message to sink-in;

✓   Know the audience. Make an attempt to know about their: fears, knowledge of the subject, learning methods, motivation, attitudes and other factors that may be influencing behaviours which include resistance to change. Relevant information could be gained by methods such as pre-event questionnaires, an introductory get-to-know session, walk-through-surveys of the workplace, attending team briefings, health and safety committee meetings and other relevant types of networks;

✓   Key messages should be clear and concise. It means, when describing a ventilation hood, listeners should be able to understand and comprehend it as a ventilation hood and not as a funnel. The information and the messages should be given in an easily accessible way;

✓   Make IIT relevant to the audience. This will help to reduce the tendency for rejecting the information or training. In other words, minimising the effect known as "it is for someone else";

✓   Make sure the information and the training methods are correct, up-to-date and can be supported with evidence. The evidence should come from credible sources, such as an independent research, enforcement bodies, legislation and authoritative publications;

✓   Use practical activities and demonstrations to communicate key messages or for developing skills. This will improve learning as well as interest. The activities chosen should be relevant to the messages, skills to be developed and the workplace situation. These are necessary for improving the attention span and to help the listener to process the information from short-term memory to long-term memory;

✓   Encourage recall and use of the information given out and the skills learnt;

✓   Messages, information and training tools used should be easy to use and are developed in consultation with those affected. This will help to create an environment in which the listeners are motivated to use the skills learnt;

✓   Risk control measures should be seen as a 'win-win' for those creating the risks (e.g. employers) and those requiring the protection (e.g. employees). They may be evaluated with the help of a "SWOT" analysis - strengths, weaknesses, opportunities and threats;

✓   Deal with myths and objections in a constructive and analytical way. The answers should be supported by credible evidence. Do not use explanation that is perceived as evidence by the trainer or someone else. The latter can create a mind-set for resisting change;

✓   Involve people from the workforce in the delivery of the training. For example, when demonstrating the correct the use of machinery, tools, PPE or skin care products;

✓   Use one-to-one approach with those "hard-to-convince". They may have an underlying perceptions and reasons for their resistance. An analysis of the issues should lead to a positive behaviour.

## DERMAL EXPOSURE CONTROL AND IIT

The main elements that would form part of any IIT for persons exposed to chemicals and wet-work can be found in relevant legislation. In this book, relevant elements can be found in Chapters 1 to 13.

### Communication Tools for Dermal Exposure Risk Management

There are many communication and training tools readily available for the professionals. Some of these are listed below and further details can be found in the further reading section at the end of this Chapter.

- Rash Decision video (HSE Books).
- Prevent work-related dermatitis – a toolbox talk (British Safety Industry Federation (BSIF) and Safety Groups UK (SGUK)).
- Occupational dermatoses (National Institute for Occupational Safety and Health – NIOSH).
- Rash Decisions Affect Your Business –Introduction to work-related dermatitis - Power point presentation (SGUK).
- Rash Decisions Affect Your Business Managing work-related dermatitis - Power point presentation (SGUK).
- Introduction to biological monitoring - Power Point Presentation (British Occupational Hygiene Society (BOHS)).
- A safety & health practitioner's guide to skin protection (Centre for Disease Control (CDC).
- 'Skin at Work' website (HSE).
- Posters on dermal exposure risk management ('Skin at Work').
- Save Our Skin (British Skin Foundation)

### Key Messages

This book is using three key messages for communicating the need for effective control of skin exposure to chemical and wet-work. These are:

- **A**void skin contact
- **P**rotect the skin and
- **C**heck for early signs of disease

The 'APC' approach is described in detail in Chapters 9, 10, 11, 12 and 13.

## EMPLOYEE PARTICIPATION

Employee involvement is essential for benefits realisation. It is an essential part of responsible risk management as explained in Appendix 3. Lord Robens said that real progress is possible only with the full co-operation and commitment of all employees. They should be able to participate fully in the making and monitoring of arrangements for safety and health at their workplace (see note below). This philosophy is supported by many research findings. They showed that organisations that involved employees, trades unions and managers achieved many benefits and these included:

- Improved health and safety performance;
- Increased ownership of risk reduction arrangements;
- Higher productivity;
- Improved relationship between managers and workers;
- Sustained behavioural changes;
- Development of practical control measures;
- Sustained implementation of control measures.

Maintaining benefits of this nature is difficult, when matters on health and safety including IIT, is considered as burdensome, constraining and business stifling. Attitudes and perceptions like these will not deliver sustained behavioural changes at all levels.

***Note:*** *The Robens Report was the product of the first comprehensive review of 'the safety and health of persons in the course of their employment'. This report was produced, in 1972, by a Royal Commission under the Chairmanship of Lord Robens.*

## CHANGING BEHAVIOURS

Experts have suggested that certain key behavioural parameters will have a significant sphere of influence on changing the behaviours of people. Addressing these issues, as applicable to a given work situation, will help to deliver sustainable outcomes. The key behavioural parameters are listed in Table 14.2. Health and safety professionals should utilise them on a regular basis for solving problems and realising benefits.

## REWARD SYSTEMS

Reward systems are used widely at work for encouraging positive behaviours and to increase performance, productivity and profits. Rewards for health and safety performance are likely to deliver desirable behaviours leading to improved health and safety. Genuine and sustained benefits can be achieved only when those affected by the risks understand the reasons for the control measures and have had a stake in developing risk reduction arrangements. Reward systems for health and safety should be directed to behaviours that sustain the correct use and maintenance of risk control measures.

Rewards can be divided into extrinsic and intrinsic types. Extrinsic rewards include profit sharing, shares, money and holidays. Intrinsic rewards include increased responsibilities, improved flexibility for self-determination of the way in which the work is delivered and public recognition. Health and safety professionals should encourage reward systems that employ a mix of extrinsic and intrinsic rewards. People affected by the reward system should be given opportunities to contribute to the development of the rewards and the procedures for awarding them.

**Table 14.2** Key parameters for behavioural changes - an example

| **Identify what behaviour is to be changed:** Wearing all-round smooth, single-use non-latex gloves when shampooing and colouring clients' hair in hairdressing establishments. | |
|---|---|
| **Key behavioural parameters**[A] | Examples of issues |
| Knowledge | What are the reasons for the need to wear gloves? Do they know the reasons and understand them? Do they know and appreciate the consequences of not wearing gloves? Do they know the benefits of wearing gloves? |
| Skills | How easy or difficult for them to implement the desired exposure control behaviours? Do they know how to correctly don and doff the gloves? |
| Self-standards | What are their views about wearing gloves? What are the reasons for the views? |
| Beliefs about capability | What are their perceived competencies on correct donning and doffing of gloves? What are their views about dermatitis and consequences and about wearing gloves. |
| Anticipated outcomes and attitudes | What do they think will happen if they wear the gloves? Look at positive and negative outcomes. What would be the personal effects of not wearing gloves? |
| Intentions and motivations | How much do they want to wear gloves? How much they feel that they need to wear gloves. Are there any conflicts and how should they be handled. Are there any incentives for wearing gloves? |
| Memory, attention and decision | Can they remember the techniques for donning and doffing of gloves? How? Will they automatically wear gloves? How much attention to detail is needed for correct donning and doffing gloves? |
| Resource constraints | To what extent resource factors will facilitate or hinder the provision of gloves and training. Are there any competing tasks and time constraints on wearing gloves? Will the employer provide gloves and will it continue in the long term? |
| Group or social influence | To what extent stakeholders (e.g. employers, managers, peers, enforcement authorities, manufactures and trade association) will help or hinder the desired outcome? What are the influences of role models in the industry? What influence will victims of dermatitis exert on glove wearing behaviour? |
| Emotions | To what extent emotional factors will hinder wearing gloves? What kind of feeling will be felt when wearing gloves? – an odd one out; manager will look at me as a trouble maker! |
| Behavioural regulation | What preparatory steps are needed to achieve the desired effect? Understand the myths about wearing gloves and develop compelling evidence based on research. What procedures and ways of working will ensure the desired effects? |
| Nature of the behaviour | Who needs to do what, when, how and how often? What is being done at present by the stakeholders? How long are the changes going to take? What systems are in place or will be put in place to achieve the desired behaviour? |

**Note:** A - These are based on Michie et al. (2005)

## CONCLUSION

This Chapter provides a concise overview to learning, risk communication, training, employee involvement, behavioural factors and reward systems. Each element is a subject on its own and could be written, explained, analysed and interpreted in many volumes. However, the information in this Chapter is intended as a "starter-pack" for delivering IIT for dermal exposure risk management. References listed in the further reading section are useful for those wishing to learn more about the subjects discussed in this Chapter.

The 'AIDAR' concept may be used as an aid for devising suitable IIT and other risk management arrangements. Ideally, risk communication and IIT should be matched to the needs of the audience, the hazards, the risks, the task and the workplace. Maximum benefits are possible only when all stakeholders have contributed to the risk control arrangements and accept responsibilities for shared ownership. Evidence- based risk management will benefit greatly if it takes account of behavioural parameters listed in Table 14.2.

## TEST YOUR KNOWLEDGE

1. Explain, how you would use the AIDAR concept for solving a dermal exposure control problem.

2. Employee involvement is one of the key aspects of strategies for implementing and maintaining effective risk control. Consider this for controlling dermal exposure (in a given task) at your workplace.

3. List the key parameters for behavioural change and apply them to a health safety situation for which you're seeking improved benefits.

## FURTHER READING

**A safety & health practitioner's guide to skin protection.** Electronic Library of Construction Occupational Safety and Health (eLCOSH). Centre for Disease Control, USA. www.cdc.gov/eLCOSH

**A primer on health risk communication principles and practices. Overview of issues and guiding principles.** Agency for Toxic Substances and Disease Registry, Depart of Health and Human Services, CDC, USA.

**Audiovisual methods in teaching (Third Edition).** E Dale. Dryden Press, New York, USA. ISBN: 00 307 3540 9.

**Clinically Orientated Anatomy** (fourth Edition). KL Moore, AF Dalley. Lippincott Williams and Wilkins, London, UK. ISBN: 0 683 06141 0.

**Health Risk Communication.** R Bowles. Health Risk Communication Office, USACHPPM. USA.

**Examples of effective worker involvement in the chemical industry.** HSE Research Report 291/2000. HSE Books, Sudbury, UK.

**Health and safety training, what you need to know (INDG345).** HSE Books, Sudbury, UK.

**HSE Human Factors Briefing Note No. 7- Safety Culture.** www.hse.gov.uk

**Human Safety and Risk Management.** AI Glendon, SG Clarke, EF Mckenna. CRC- Taylor and Francis, Abingdon, Oxfordshire, UK. ISBN: 0 8493 3090 4.

**Making psychological theory useful for implementing evidence based practice: a consensus approach.** S Michie, M Johnston, C Abraham, R Lawton, D Parker, A Walker. Quality and Safety of Health Care; 14 (2005): 26-33.

**Occupational Dermatoses.** National Institute for Occupational Safety and Health (NIOSH), USA. www.cdc.gov.

**Prevent work-related dermatitis – It's In Your Hands (rev.1.0)** – a toolbox talk. British Safety Industry Federation. www.bsif.co.uk and Safety Groups UK. www.rospa.com/safetygroupsuk

**Rash decisions affect your business – An introduction to work-related contact dermatitis.** Safety Groups UK (SGUK), UK.

**Rash Decisions** (a video). HSE Books, Sudbury, UK.

**Risk Communication, A guide to regulatory practice.** HSE, UK.

**Skin at Work.** Health and Safety Executive, UK. www.hse.gov.uk/skin

**Teaching Today – A practical guide.** G Petty. Nelson Thorns, Cheltenham, UK. ISBN: 0 7487 8525 6.

**The Changing Nature of Occupational Health.** R McCaig, M Harrington. HSE Books, Sudbury, UK. ISBN: 0 7176 1665 7.

**The Psychology of Selling and Advertising.** EK Strong. McGraw-Hill Book Company, New York, USA.

**The role and effectiveness of safety representatives in influencing workplace safety.** Research Report No. 363. HSE, UK.

**Save Our Skin.** British Skin Foundation. www.brtishskinfoundation.org.uk

**Theories of Selling.** EK Strong. Journal of Applied Psychology; 9 (1925): 75-86.

**Unions, safety committees and workplace injuries (Discussion paper series 31).** P Paci, B Reilly, P Holl. City University, London, UK.

**Unlock the potential.** J Manson. Safety and Health Practitioner; December (2005): 37-39.

**WISHful thinking.** R Cooling. Safety and Health Practitioner; November (2005): 43-45.

**Worker participation in change process in a Danish industrial setting.** K Rasmussen, DJ Glasscock, ON Hansen, O Carstensen, JF Jepsen, KJ Nielsen. American Journal of Industrial Medicine; 49 (2006): 767-779.

# *Appendix 1*

# Glossary of Terms

| Terms used in the book | Explanation |
|---|---|
| Absorption | A process by which one substance takes up another. For example $CO_2$ dissolved in water, a chemical dissolving in another and tissues taking up fluids or chemicals. Horny layer cells taking up water. |
| Acne | A common inflammatory disorder of the sebaceous glands (see *oil glands*). |
| Activator proteins | Cytokines: protein molecules released by cells when activated by allergens. They initiate immune responses. Examples of cytokines include lymphokines and interleukins. |
| | Histamine. This is found in nearly all tissues of the body and associated with cells called "mast cells". Large amounts are released following skin damage or irritation causing the production of flare up and weals. For example, histamine is released when a sensitised person is exposed to latex rubber proteins. |
| Adequate control | Exposure control measures can be considered as adequate, if they can provide a level of protection required to reduce the exposure to comply with the law. |
| Adsorption | An adhesion of a layer of molecules to a solid surface. Gases trapped in cavities found in porous material such as activated charcoal. Adsorbed gases can be released by heating the charcoal. |
| Allergen /Allergenic substance | Allergen – any substance that causes an allergy in a hypersensitive person. There are different types of allergens; they affect different tissues and organs. Examples of allergens include latex proteins, chromium, pollens, fur, house mites, drugs, and cosmetics. Other terms meaning the same thing are: antigen (normally used to refer to proteins, a substance combining with protein to become an allergen may be called the same); and hapten. |
| Approved Code of Practices (ACoPs) | ACoPs in the UK have a special legal status. If a person (e.g. an employer) is prosecuted for breach of health and safety law, and it is proved that the person did not follow the relevant provision of a given Code, the person will need to show that he/she has complied with the law in some other way or a court will find the person at fault. |
| Base layer | Stratum germinativum, stratum basale or basal layer. |
| Base layer cells | Keratinocytes from which other cells of the outer layer of the skin are formed. |
| Between-the-cells route | Intercellular route. Spaces found between adjacent cells. |
| Biological agent | It can be a ***micro-organism***, ***cell culture***, or human endoparasite (a parasite that live inside its host). These agents create a hazard to human health such as infection, disease, allergy or sensitisation, toxicity and rash. |

| Terms used in the book | Explanation |
| --- | --- |
| Caucasians | A person with white/pale yellow skin. |
| Cell culture | Growing of cells outside the body in an artificial growth medium. |
| Depigmentation | White or pale skin. ***Vitiligo.*** |
| Diffusion | Process by which chemicals move through the skin, from high concentration side (skin surface) to low concentration side (inside the skin). It means concentration gradient is one of the important elements determining the rate of chemical uptake via the skin. |
| Dry and scaly skin | Ichthyosis, a genetically determined skin disorder in which there is abnormal scaling of the skin. |
| Eruption | An outbreak of a rash or blisters on the skin. |
| Fatty tissue | Adipose tissue. A fibrous connective tissue packed with lots of fat containing cells. Food in excess of requirements is converted into fat and stored within these cells. |
| Foreign bodies | Antigens – any substances that the body regards as foreign or potentially dangerous. |
| Free radicals | Highly reactive and dangerous molecules. |
| Frontline | In the context of this book, it includes people at production sites (e.g. Foreman) and site or plant health and safety officers. |
| Genetic make-up | Endogenous – arising within or derived from the body. An inherited condition. |
| Granular layer | Stratum granulosum. |
| Hazardous agents | These include "*hazardous substances*" (see below), UV, IR, microwave and ionising radiation, hot and cold environments, and mechanical forces. |
| Hazardous substances | Chemicals and chemical preparations and products labelled as irritants, corrosive, harmful, toxic and very toxic; substances which have occupational exposure limits, skin notation, biological monitoring guidance values; biological agents; natural products which can cause ill health including skin diseases; wet-work. |
| Healthy bacteria | In the context of this book, bacteria resident on the skin and are essential for the correct protective functioning of the skin. |
| Histamine | This is found in nearly all tissues of the body and associated with a cell called "mast cell". Large amounts are released following skin damage or irritation causing the production of flare up and weal. |
| Histological response | A response arsing from a tissue. |
| Horny layer | Stratum corneum or corneocytes. Horny layer means its cells are toughened like an animal's horn. |
| Immune response/ Immunological response | The response of the immune system (the body's protective system) to the presence of antigens (foreign bodies, such as an allergic substance). The body's ability to resist infection with the help of antibodies and white blood cells. |
| Inner section | Hypodermis, subcutis or subcutaneous layer |
| Langerhans Cells (LC) | The cells discovered by Langerhans in 1860. These are dendritic type cells (cells with specialised allergen presenting function). They connect to other cells using tentacles. The major antigen (allergen)-capturing and presenting cells of the skin. |

| Terms used in the book | Explanation |
|---|---|
| Lucid layer | Stratum lucidum |
| Lymph node | One of a number of small swellings in the lymphatic system. It acts as a filter for the lymph, preventing foreign substances from entering the bloodstream. They also produce lymphocytes (white blood cells). |
| Lymphatic vessels | A vast net work of vessels throughout the body which transports a watery fluid known as lymph. They receive excess fluid - water and dissolved electrolytes such as sodium, potassium and chloride ions; and proteins from tissue/cell fluids. These vessels connect to the blood system and carry substances concerned with the immune system. |
| Lymphokine | A substance produced by the lymphocytes (white blood cells) and has a role in immunological function. |
| Mast cell | A large cell in connective tissues. These cells contain histamine. |
| Melanin | Pigment formed by the melonocytes. The brown/black form is called Eumelanin and the red or yellow form is called phaemelanin. |
| Metabolites | Substances formed when the body converts food to release energy or chemicals that have gained entry, such as paracetamol. |
| Micro-organism | A microbiological entity made up of cells (e.g. a fungus) or without cells (e.g. a virus) and is capable of replication or transferring genetic material. |
| Middle section | Dermis or Corium. |
| Oedema | Excessive accumulation of fluid in the skin. |
| Oil glands | Sebaceous glands. These secrete an oily substance, sebum, which is composed of fatty acids, waxes and fat. |
| Outer section | Epidermis. |
| Outside agents | Exogenous – outside the body. |
| Pathological response | Relates to or arising from disease caused by a pathogen such as a bacteria. |
| Physiological response | Cells or an organ related response |
| Pigment-forming cells | Melonocytes. See melanin. |
| Pigmentary disorders | Vitiligo. A common disorder in which white or pale patches appear on the skin. Certain chemicals can cause this disorder. Loss of pigment in areas of the skin, resulting in the appearance of white patches or bands. |
| Potency | Power. |
| Pressure difference | Interstitial pressure. |
| Prickle cell layer | Stratum spinosum. |
| Reasonably practicable | Where the cost in money, time and trouble (effort) is not grossly disproportionate to the improvement achieved in protecting the employees health and safety. It means an assessment should be made in which the quantum of risk is placed in one scale and the sacrifice, whether in money, time or trouble, involved in the measures necessary to avoid the risk is placed in the other. Ultimately, the courts would decide whether an employer has taken all the reasonably practicable measures for achieving adequate control. |

| Terms used in the book | Explanation |
|---|---|
| Scaling skin condition | Psoriasis, a chronic skin condition in which scaly pink patches form on elbows, knees scalp and other parts of the body. |
| Substances hazardous to health | This term has a legal meaning within COSHH. In summary, substances or preparation carrying the very toxic, toxic, harmful, corrosive or irritant symbol; substances and products with occupational exposure limits known as workplace exposure limits (WELs); a biological agent, dusts of an kind and not covered by other categories and the concentration in air equal to or greater than 10mg/m3 (inhalable) and 4mg/m3 (respirable). |
| Suitable and sufficient | The measures taken are appropriate to the risk or risks involved and it is reasonably practicable for prevention or adequate control of the risk or risks involved without increasing the overall risks. |
| T-cell | It is also known as T-lymphocyte. It is responsible for capturing, suppressing or killing certain types of allergens or foreign bodies. There are three types of T-cells to do the desired work. |
| Tentacles | It means an elongated and flexible structure. |
| Through-the-cell route | transcellular route. |
| Ties | Desmosome - an area of contact between two adjacent cells. These may be viewed as "protein bridges" or as similar to stabilising pins that keep rail tracks firm at a set width. |
| Tolerable | Measures taken to control a specified health or safety risk has satisfied the requirements of "reasonably practicable". |
| Valid technique | In the context of health surveillance, it means techniques that are precise enough to detect something wrong that could be caused by exposure to a particular health hazard and which is safe and practicable in the workplace setting. |
| Vesiculation | A very small blister in the skin, often no bigger than a pin point that contains a clear fluid. |
| Vitiligo | A condition in which light-coloured blotchy patches appear on the skin as results of localised loss of the pigment melanin. |
| Wet-work | Wet-work means having hands repeatedly wet or wet for long periods during the working day. As a general guide, it means having hands wet for more than two hours a day or washing hands more than 20 times a day. Frequent contact with water or water mixed with chemicals. |
| White blood cells | Leucocyte – any blood cell that contains a nucleus. They are involved in protecting the body against foreign sentences and antibody production. |
| Yeasts | Any group of fungi the "body" (mycelium) consists of individual cells. |

# *Appendix 2*

# Figures and Tables List

# *Appendix 3*

# Sensible Risk Management

The principles listed below are essential elements of "sensible risk management" and should be applied to protect employees and public from real harm and suffering.

- Ensuring that workers and the public are properly protected;

- Providing overall benefit to society by balancing benefits and risks, with a focus on reducing real risks, which arise more often and those with serious consequences for health and safety;

- Enabling innovation, research, development and learning, not stifling them;

- Ensuring that those who create risks manage them responsibly and understand that failure to manage real risks responsibly is likely to lead to robust action by the regulators and courts; and

- Enabling individuals to understand that as well as the right to protection, they also have to exercise responsibility.

In other words, a sensible risk management ***is not*** about:

- Creating a totally risk-free society and workplaces;

- Generating useless paperwork;

- Scaring people by exaggerating or creating fuss or publicity about trivial risks;

- Reducing or allowing less protection of people from risks that cause real harm and suffering;

- Stopping research and innovation;

- Creating barriers against profitability; or

- Stopping important recreational and learning activities for individuals.

**Principles of sensible risk management.**
Health and Safety Executive, London, UK. http://www.hse.gov.uk/risk/principles

# *Index*